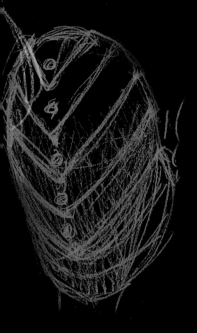

Jodorowsy   Gimenez

The Metabarons ™

Path of the Warrior

Jodorowsy   Gimenez

The Metabarons ™

Path of the Warrior

ORIGINAL METABARON CHARACTER CREATED BY MŒBIUS AND JODOROWSKY

STORY BY
ALEXANDRO JODOROWSKY

ART & COLOR BY
JUAN GIMENEZ

COVER ART BY
JUAN GIMENEZ

ENGLISH TRANSLATION BY
**JULIA SOLIS
& JUSTIN KELLY**

EDITED BY
**PHILIPPE HAURI
& BRUNO LECIGNE**

ADDITIONAL BOOK TEXT
**ADRIAN A. CRUZ
& IAN SATTLER**

LOGOS DESIGNED BY
DIDIER GONORD

COLLECTION DESIGNED BY
THIERRY FRISSEN

HUMANOIDS PUBLISHING™

Chairman & Publisher
FABRICE GIGER

Literary Director
PHILIPPE HAURI

Director of Publishing U.S.
DAVE OLBRICH

Director of Finance and Administration
PAM SHRIVER

Managing Editor
ADRIAN A. CRUZ

Marketing Manager
IAN SATTLER

Graphic Designer
THIERRY FRISSEN

Circulation
KAREN BAYLY, SUE HARTUNG

Licensing & Development
JUSTIN CONNOLLY

PUBLISHED BY
HUMANOIDS PUBLISHING
(in association with Les Humanoïdes Associés)
PO Box 931658 Hollywood, CA 90093

ISBN #1-930652-47-X
First Printing March 2001

This book collects the stories originally published in English as
The Metabarons #1-#5 by Humanoids Publishing.

THE METABARONS™: PATH OF THE WARRIOR

PRINTED IN EUROPE

THE ORIGIN OF THE METABARON

"Ever since the second book of The Incal, in which the character of the Metabaron is introduced, I had the feeling there were other stories to be told about him. This hero, presented as the ultimate warrior, suddenly turns up in The Incal, without any explanation or background. The mystery had to be explored."

ALEXANDRO JODOROWSKY

The Metabaron first appeared in May 1981 with the first French printing of Moebius' and Jodorwosky's The Incal. Only one of a cast of characters that shaped the adventures of John Difool, the Metabaron remained an important yet mysterious part of the story. Six French volumes were released in The Incal album series, each featuring the Metabaron, making him a prominent feature in the European comic book scene throughout the eighties. The Incal was first seen on American shores in three soft-cover editions printed by Marvel/Epic in 1988; thus introducing the Metabaron to America more than a decade before his comic book series would finally grace store racks. Meanwhile Jodorowsky continued to expand the world of John Difool with a French album series called "Before the Incal" and again the Metabaron's presence was felt, though not yet in his own series as Jodorowsky envisioned. He had always admired the work of Juan Gimenez and The Saga of the Metabarons seemed the perfect project for collaboration. In the early nineties a deal was sealed and the journey began. Beginning with the recreation of a short Metabarons origins story, originally drawn by Moebius, Gimenez set to work (see page 157).

Initially conceived as two French albums, The Saga of the Metabarons proved to be so popular with readers that new albums were created, continuing the lineage of the ultimate warrior. Jodorowsky and Gimenez are currently completing the seventh French album in the series.

Since it's arrival on American shores The Metabarons has garnered not only acclaim from critics, creators and fans; it has also spawned a role-playing game. The character also appears in a new series, The Dreamshifters, illustrated by Travis Charest to be released in 2002.

Artwork by Mœbius

YES! BUT A REAL ONE THIS TIME! NOT ONE OF THOSE SILLY ROBOT TALES...

I KNOW, I KNOW... ONLY HUMAN STORIES CAN REALLY STIMULATE OUR CIRCUITS...

VERY WELL, I WILL TELL YOU A STORY ABOUT ATHE METABARON, MY MASTER, WHO HAS BEEN ABSENT FOR THREE MONTHS, TWELVE DAYS, 6 HOURS, 4 MINUTES AND 15 SECONDS STANDARD TIME.

THE METABARON! HE IS THE MOST SAVAGELY UNPREDICTABLE HUMAN OF ALL!

HE IS THE GREATEST! HE IS THE META-WARRIOR! BUT I LOVE HIM FOR HIS BIONIC PARTS!

WELL, MOST HUMANS HAVE BIONIC PROSTHESES...

TRUE, BUT THESE ARE JUST ACCESSORY ORGANS... POOR HUMANS... NO, THE METABARON HAS A BIONIC EAR AND BIONIC LOBES IN THE RIGHT HALF OF HIS BRAIN... AND I'M NOT TALKING "TOPAZ" CHIPS HERE!

TOPAZ CHIPS!...HA! HA!... BUT HOW CAN THAT BE, TONTO ? DOES THAT MEAN HE WAS BORN LIKE THAT?

HA! HA! HA! OF COURSE NOT, YOU FOOL! ROBOTS TEND TO FORGET THAT HUMANS ARE BORN JUST FLESH AND BLOOD!

NO, IT HAS TO DO WITH WHAT MY ABSENT MASTER ONCE CALLED THE INITIATORY TRADITION OF THE META-WARRIORS. LISTEN! I WILL TELL YOU THE STORY AS I KNOW IT...

8

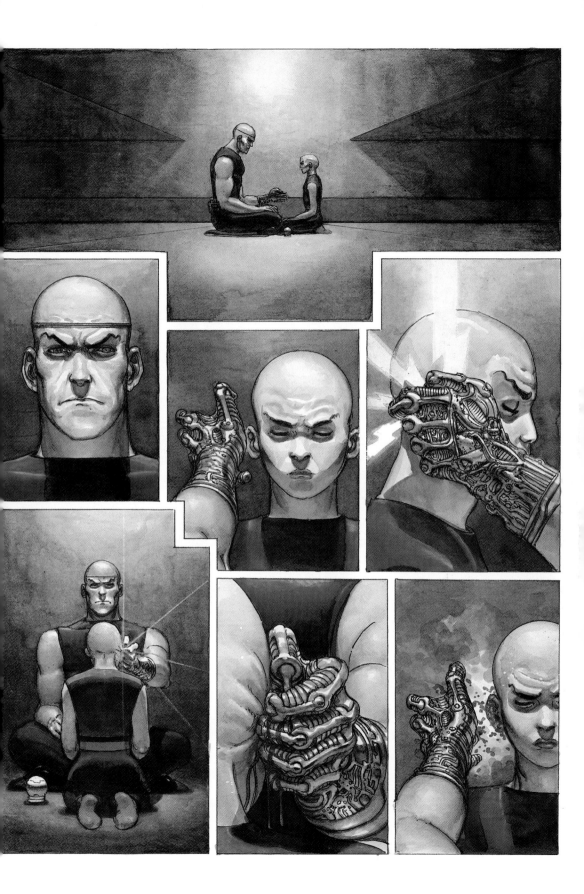

YOU AREN'T CRYING!

AND YOU, FATHER, DID YOU CRY DURING YOUR INITIATION?

I REMAINED IMPASSIVE, JUST LIKE YOU... BUT I COULDN'T PREVENT A TEAR FROM ESCAPING.

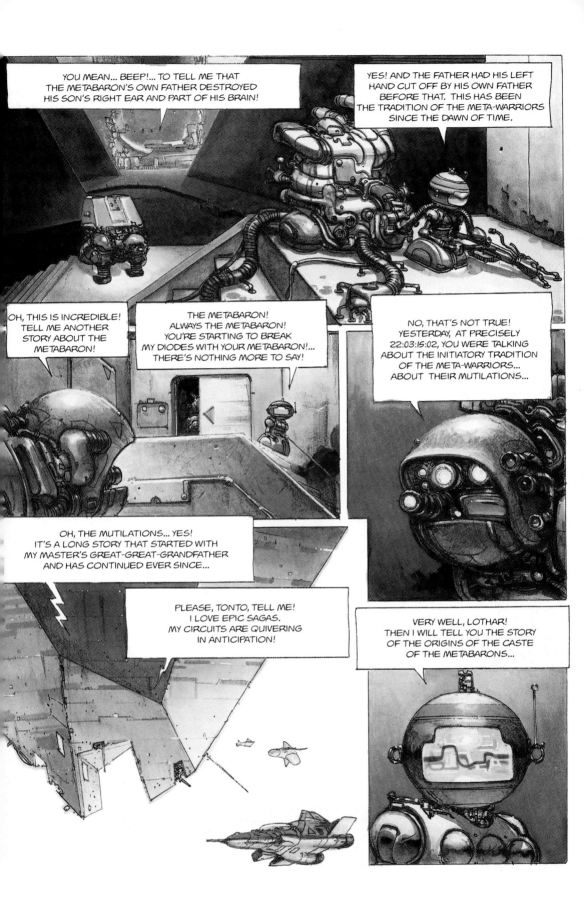

YOU MEAN... BEEP!... TO TELL ME THAT THE METABARON'S OWN FATHER DESTROYED HIS SON'S RIGHT EAR AND PART OF HIS BRAIN!

YES! AND THE FATHER HAD HIS LEFT HAND CUT OFF BY HIS OWN FATHER BEFORE THAT. THIS HAS BEEN THE TRADITION OF THE META-WARRIORS SINCE THE DAWN OF TIME.

OH, THIS IS INCREDIBLE! TELL ME ANOTHER STORY ABOUT THE METABARON!

THE METABARON! ALWAYS THE METABARON! YOU'RE STARTING TO BREAK MY DIODES WITH YOUR METABARON!... THERE'S NOTHING MORE TO SAY!

NO, THAT'S NOT TRUE! YESTERDAY, AT PRECISELY 22:03:15:02, YOU WERE TALKING ABOUT THE INITIATORY TRADITION OF THE META-WARRIORS... ABOUT THEIR MUTILATIONS...

OH, THE MUTILATIONS... YES! IT'S A LONG STORY THAT STARTED WITH MY MASTER'S GREAT-GREAT-GRANDFATHER AND HAS CONTINUED EVER SINCE...

PLEASE, TONTO, TELL ME! I LOVE EPIC SAGAS. MY CIRCUITS ARE QUIVERING IN ANTICIPATION!

VERY WELL, LOTHAR! THEN I WILL TELL YOU THE STORY OF THE ORIGINS OF THE CASTE OF THE METABARONS...

OTHON VON SALZA, MY MASTER'S GREAT-GREAT-GRANDFATHER, WAS ONCE AN INTERGALACTIC PIRATE
WHO FINALLY SUCCEEDED IN WINNING THE HAND OF THE BEAUTIFUL BUT INDOMITABLE LADY EDNA.
SHE WAS THE DAUGHTER OF THE BARON BERARD OF CASTAKA, UNDISPUTED RULER OF THE PLANET MARMOLA
IN THE PHILORIAN SYSTEM... HOWEVER, EDNA'S AMBIGUOUS FEMININITY HAD ONLY BORN OTHON ONE SON, BARI...

MARMOLA WAS A GIGANTIC MARBLE GLOBE WITH ONLY A SMALL, FERTILE VALLEY, HOUSING THE FORTRESS OF
CASTAKA. IT COULD SUBSIST BY SELLING ITS PRECIOUS MARBLE TO THE BUILDERS OF THE IMPERIAL PALACES.
THE MARMOLANS THUS LIVED A LIFE OF TRANQUIL PEACE AND HAPPINESS, UNTIL THE UNEXPECTED ARRIVAL
OF A CARGO SHIP FROM THE IMPERIAL MERCHANTS GUILD...

THIS IS THE PLANET-QUARRY, YOUR EMINENCE!
THERE'S ENOUGH MARBLE DOWN THERE
TO PAVE ALL THE STREETS OF TECHNOGEA...

HIS HIGHNESS THE TECHNO-POPE
ONLY NEEDS ENOUGH TO ERECT
HIS NEW TEMPLE- BANK.
I THINK A THOUSAND BLOCKS
SHOULD BE SUFFICIENT...

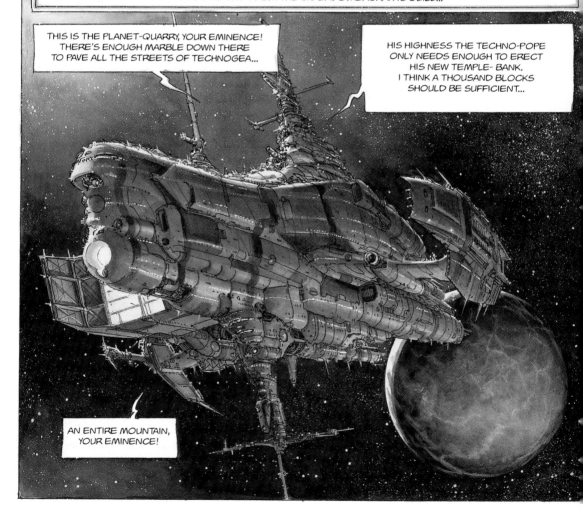

AN ENTIRE MOUNTAIN,
YOUR EMINENCE!

14

15

17

18

YOU'VE BEEN RAISED AS A WARRIOR, BARI! YOU'RE NOT SUPPOSED TO KNOW DISTRESS, CONFUSION OR FEAR! YOUR FATHER MUST BE SACRIFICED!

IF WE RESCUE HIM, THE EMPIRE WILL DISCOVER WHAT HAS BEEN OUR SECRET FOR GENERATIONS, AND GALACTIC PEACE WILL END OVERNIGHT!

YOU'RE RIGHT, GRANDFATHER! I'M SORRY! MY FATHER WILL KNOW HOW TO DIE LIKE A HERO!

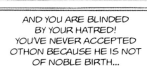

NO! NEVER! OTHON WILL LIVE!

LOVE IS BLINDING YOU, DAUGHTER!

AND YOU ARE BLINDED BY YOUR HATRED! YOU'VE NEVER ACCEPTED OTHON BECAUSE HE IS NOT OF NOBLE BIRTH...

... BUT ACCIDENTS HAPPEN FOR A REASON! BY PRESERVING YOUR CHERISHED SECRET, YOU'VE KEPT PROGRESS AT BAY. MAYBE IT'S TIME FOR THE GALAXY TO BREAK FREE OF ITS ANTI-G TECHNOLOGY AND ENTER A NEW ERA. WE'RE READY TO FACE THE FUTURE!

20

DO YOU SEE WHAT I SEE, YOUR EMINENCE?

YES, MAGNATE! I SEE THE GREATEST TECHNICAL REVOLUTION OF THIS CENTURY!

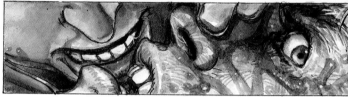

THIS IS A MISTAKE! YOU SHOULD HAVE LET ME DIE! NOW OUR PEACEFUL EXISTENCE IS OVER!

MY SON-IN-LAW AT LAST PROVES WORTHY OF OUR HERITAGE!

NOW WE ARE FORCED TO KILL OUR VISITORS...

NO! YOU MUST STOP THINKING LIKE THE PIRATE YOU ONCE WERE, OTHON! ONCE I'M DEAD, YOU'LL BE THE NEW BARON, AND WILL HAVE TO UPHOLD OUR OATH OF LOYALTY TOWARDS THE EMPIRE!

BUT...

SILENCE! LET'S GIVE THEM THEIR MARBLE. THEN WE MUST PREPARE TO FACE THE COMING UPHEAVALS WITH DIGNITY!

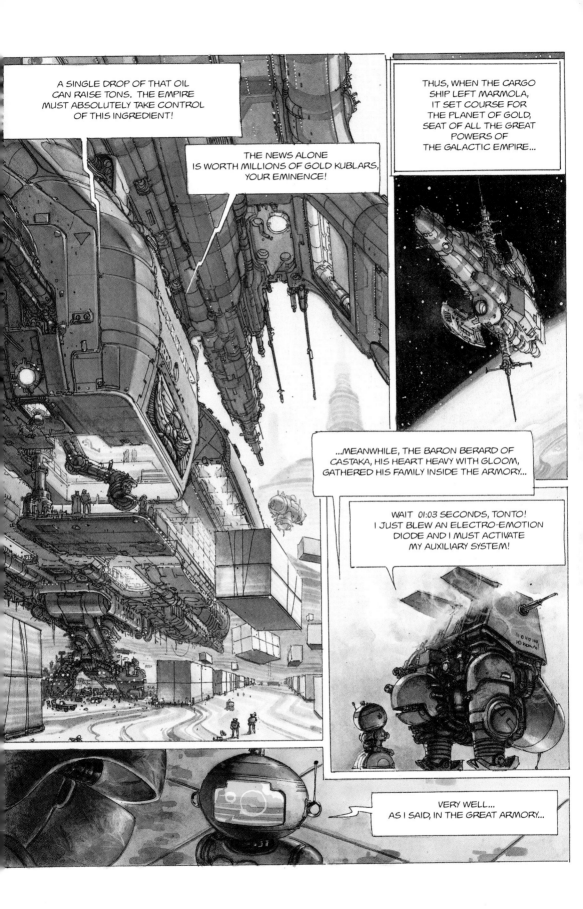

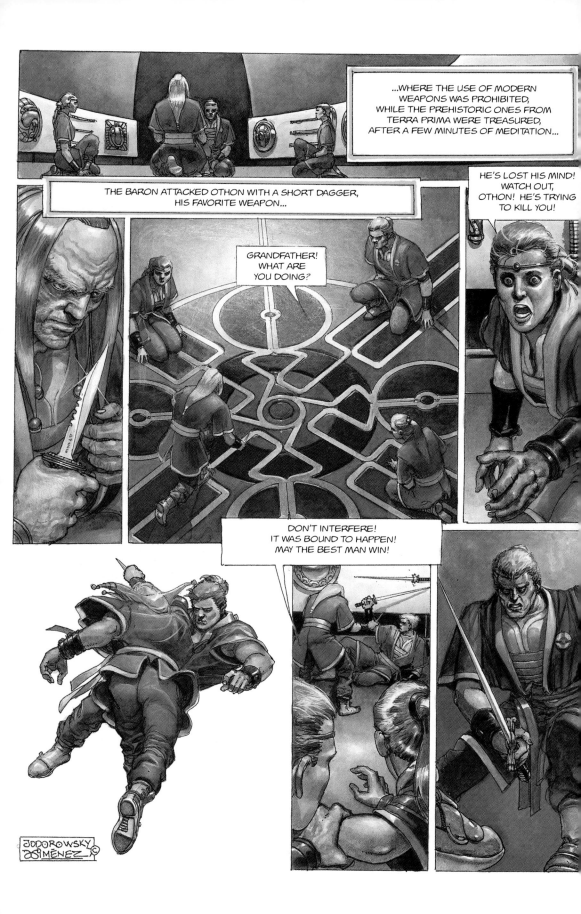

...WHERE THE USE OF MODERN WEAPONS WAS PROHIBITED, WHILE THE PREHISTORIC ONES FROM TERRA PRIMA WERE TREASURED, AFTER A FEW MINUTES OF MEDITATION...

THE BARON ATTACKED OTHON WITH A SHORT DAGGER, HIS FAVORITE WEAPON...

HE'S LOST HIS MIND! WATCH OUT, OTHON! HE'S TRYING TO KILL YOU!

GRANDFATHER! WHAT ARE YOU DOING?

DON'T INTERFERE! IT WAS BOUND TO HAPPEN! MAY THE BEST MAN WIN!

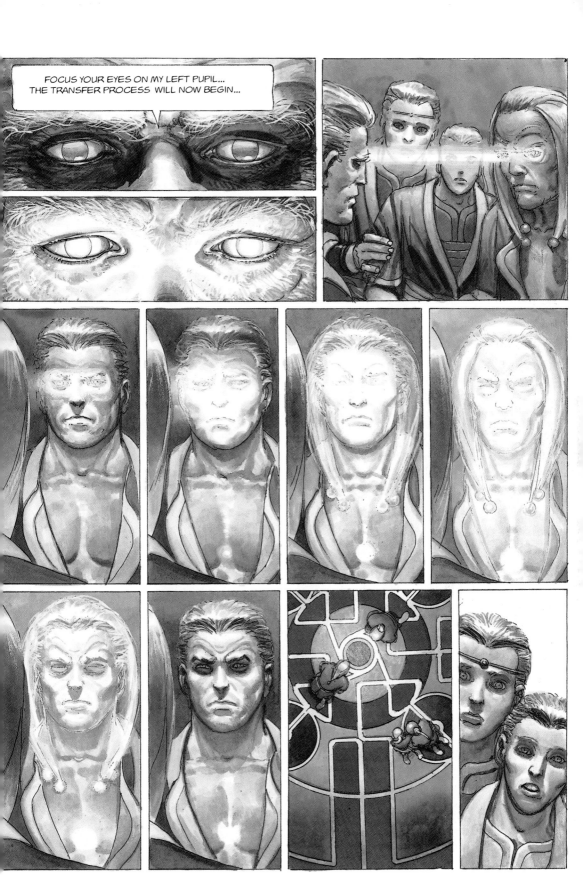

28

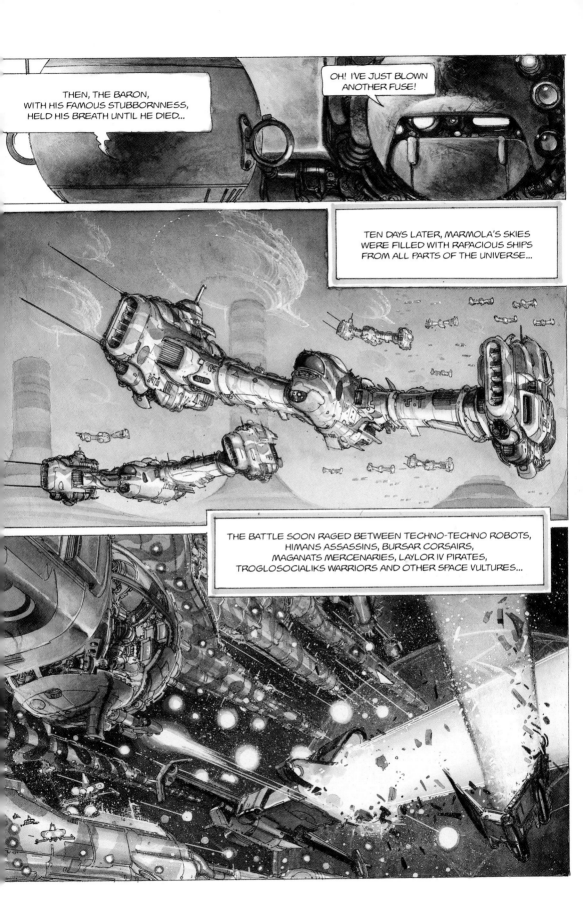

LISTEN TO ME!

HALT!

YOU ARE THE IMPERIAL COUPLE'S PRIVATE GUARDS! HOW DARE YOU DISOBEY THEM LIKE THIS? A WARRIOR WHO NEGLECTS HIS DUTY IS BUT A PITIFUL COWARD!

...REGAIN YOUR DIGNITY! REFUSE TO OBEY YOUR TREACHEROUS AND POWER-HUNGRY GENERALS!

FIRE!

DEAD FOR NO REASON, EXCEPT HER OWN PRIDE. WHAT A WASTE

SO MY FATHER IS A COWARD! HE BROKE MY LEGS BECAUSE HE WAS AFRAID TO SEE ME FIGHT!

WHO WILL BE BRAVE ENOUGH TO CARRY ME OUT TO MY MOTHER'S REMAINS? I WANT TO DIE AS SHE DID. AS A HERO!

ENOUGH, BARI! I WANT YOU ALIVE. YOUR RECKLESSNESS COULD GET US ALL KILLED!

A WARRIOR'S HONOR IS NOT EARNED IN DEATH, BUT IN VICTORY! DECEPTION CAN BE AN HONORABLE WEAPON TOO!

THE ENDOGUARDS' WEAPONS ARE POWERFUL, BUT THEY CAN ONLY KILL FROM A DISTANCE...

YOU HAVE NO HONOR!

34

THOSE BATTALIONS FORGOT THE ART OF FIGHTING MAN-TO-MAN CENTURIES AGO... AND AS FOR US, WE'RE TRAINED FOR IT!

THE BARON USED TO SAY: "EVEN WHEN THEY OUTNUMBER YOU, ONLY YOUR WILLINGNESS TO DESTROY EVERY LAST ONE OF YOUR ENE-MIES WILL LEAD YOU TO VICTORY!"

YOU, HOHENHOLE, WILL ATTACK FROM THE NORTH WITH HALF OUR MEN. ENGAGE THEM AS CLOSELY AS POSSIBLE, AND TRY TO FIGHT MAN-TO-MAN!

AND YOU, KONRATH, WILL DO THE SAME FROM THE SOUTH. YOU MUST FORCE THE ENDOGUARDS TO REMAIN TIGHTLY PACKED TOGETHER. COME OUT FROM THE SECRET TUNNELS.

AS FOR ME, I'LL ATTACK THEM RIGHT IN THE CEN-TER!

HURL THOSE BLOCKS, MEN! DON'T LET EVEN ONE OF THESE BLACK DOGS GAIN AN INCH! DUTY MAY WEIGH HEAVIER THAN A MOUNTAIN, BUT DEATH IS AS LIGHT AS A FEATHER!

FIGHT HARD, FRIENDS! ADVANCE TO THE TUNE OF MY FIFE! THESE METALLIC MONKEYS...

...ARE NOT AS TOUGH AS THEY LOOK! "IN THE NAME OF VICTORY, ALL IS PERMITTED..."

WHILE THE TWINS, KONRATH AND HOHENHOLE, BARELY PROTECTED BY THEIR LEVITATING BLOCKS OF MARBLE, HELD BACK THE ENDO-GUARDS WITH SUICIDAL COURAGE, OTHON, ARMED ONLY WITH A SHORT DAGGER, APPROA-CHED THE HEART OF THE ENEMY FORCES THROUGH A NARROW UNDERGROUND PASSAGEWAY...

WHAT CHIP-WRACKING SUSPENSE! MY CIR-CUITS ARE OVERHEA-TING. COULD YOU GET ME A LITTLE DRINK OF ULTRA-COOLANT?

DEATH!!!

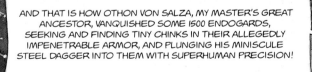

AND THAT IS HOW OTHON VON SALZA, MY MASTER'S GREAT ANCESTOR, VANQUISHED SOME 1500 ENDOGARDS, SEEKING AND FINDING TINY CHINKS IN THEIR ALLEGEDLY IMPENETRABLE ARMOR, AND PLUNGING HIS MINISCULE STEEL DAGGER INTO THEM WITH SUPERHUMAN PRECISION!

YOU MUST BE SO PROUD OF HIM, TONTO! HAVE ANO-THER DRINK OF ULTRA-COOLANT WITH ME!

37

THE VALLEY, LITTERED WITH CORPSES, RESEMBLED A SILENT, BLACK LAKE...

OTHON MADE HIS WAY TO THE NORTHERN BATTLEFIELD, SEARCHING FOR HIS LIEUTENANT, HOHENHOLE...

...THEN HEADED BACK SOUTH TO RECOVER THE BODY OF HIS OTHER LOYAL FRIEND, KONRATH...

ONLY THEN DID HE PAY A FINAL TRIBUTE TO HIS WIFE EDNA, AT THE BASE OF THE COLUMN WHERE HER BODY HAD BEEN DISINTEGRATED...

YOU FOLLOWED THE TEACHINGS OF YOUR FATHER AND MASTER: "THE VALIANT WARRIOR THINKS NEITHER OF VICTORY NOR DEFEAT..."

40

I UNDERSTAND YOUR FEELINGS, MY SON... BUT I MUST TELL YOU THAT DESPITE EVERYTHING WE WILL HAVE TO NEGOTIATE WITH THE EMPIRE... YES... DESPITE EVERYTHING, OUR EPYPHITE WILL BE TARNISHED.

BY VIRTUE OF INTER-STELLAR SPIES, WORD OF THE GREAT DEEDS OF OTHON, THE NEW BARON OF THE CASTAKAS, SPREAD ACROSS THE ENTIRE GALAXY...

A WEEK LATER, THE IMPERIAL COUPLE'S GOLDEN VESSEL, NOW ACCOMPANIED BY A NEW, PURPLE ENDOGUARD, ARRIVED AT MARMOLA...

OTHON AND BARI WERE CONGRATULATED AND REWARDED, THEN...

...IN A PRIVATE CHAMBER, NEGOTIATIONS BEGAN...

YOUR MAJESTIES... MY SON AND I ARE THE ONLY ONES WHO KNOW THE SECRET OF THE EPYPHITE. NO AMOUNT OF TORTURE WILL MAKE US REVEAL IT... AND IF YOU TRY TO FIND IT WITHOUT US, YOU'LL SPEND YEARS SEARCHING FOR IT ON THIS IMMENSE PLANET...

THE ENTIRE EMPIRE IMPATIENTLY AWAITS AN AGREEMENT. SPEAK, BARON! WHAT ARE YOUR TERMS?

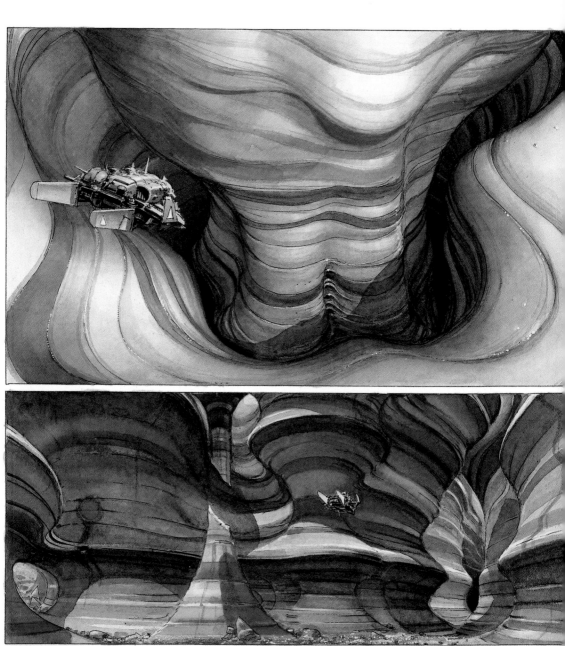

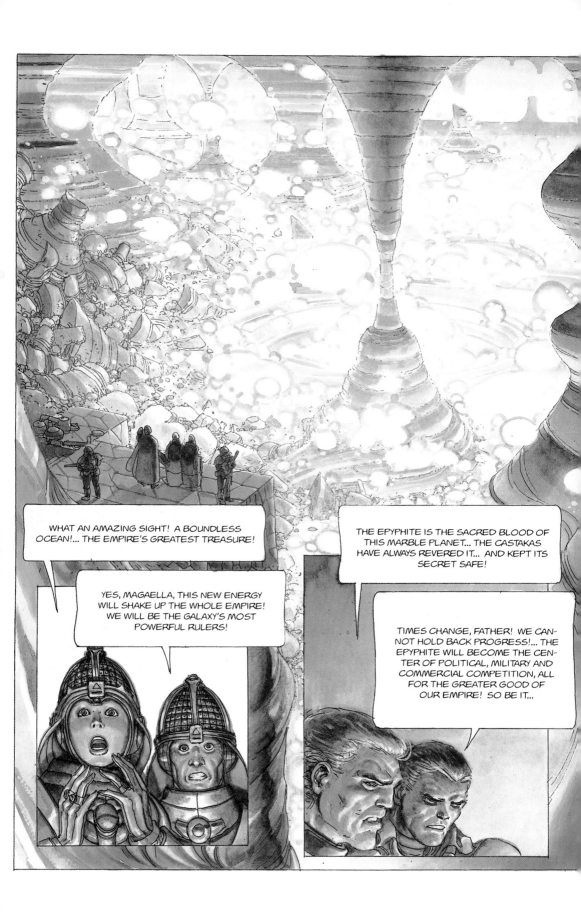

BUT TELL ME, TONTO... DID THEY GET WHAT THEY ASKED FOR, OR WERE THEY SWINDLED?

AH, LOTHAR, YOUR SKEPTICAL CIRCUITS MAKE YOU DOUBT EVERYTHING, EVEN THE IMPERIAL WORD! THEY WERE GRANTED THE REASONABLE PERCENTAGE THEY HAD REQUESTED OF THE EPYPHITE SALES. THAT BECAME THE FOUNDATION OF THE METABARONS' UNLIMITED FORTUNE...

ALL WELL AND GOOD, TONTO! BUT DID THEY GET THE NEW AND FERTILE PLANET TO WHICH THEY COULD TRANSFER THE CASTAKA FORTRESS STONE BY STONE?

YES, LOTHAR... STONE BY STONE... THEY INHERITED THE MAGNIFICENT WORLD OF OKHAR, IN THE DIAMOND CONSTELLATION...

AND BARI'S PRESENT? DID THEY RECEIVE THAT? YOU STILL HAVEN'T TOLD ME WHAT OTHON REQUESTED... SURELY SOMETHING EXTRAORDINARY! I CAN'T IMAGINE WHAT WOULD BRING BACK JOY TO A YOUNG WARRIOR HANDICAPPED FOR LIFE...

YES, LOTHAR... WHEN THEY FINALLY SETTLED ON OKHAR, THEY RECEIVED A MARVELOUS GIFT!

WHAT WAS IT? TELL ME QUICKLY, BEFORE MY CIRCUITS MELT!

IT WAS A HORSE, LOTHAR! A LIVING SPECIMEN OF A BREED THAT HAD BEEN EXTINCT FOR 20,000 YEARS, EVER SINCE THE SIXTH WORLD WAR! ITS GENES HAD BEEN CONSERVED IN THE IMPERIAL PALACE'S GENETIC MUSEUM...

AND THE COST? 100 TONS OF GOLD! THE LAST EQUINE OF ALL THE GALAXIES, BROUGHT BACK TO LIFE BY THE LABORS OF AN ARMY OF TECHNO-TECHNO SCIENTISTS!

WOW!

I DON'T HAVE THE WORDS TO THANK YOU, FATHER! IF ONE DAY I MANAGE TO RIDE THIS LIVING MIRACLE, REST ASSURED THAT MY TASTE FOR LIFE WILL RETURN!

THIS ANIMAL WAS BORN ONLY FOR YOU, BARI! GIVE HIM A LUMP OF SUGAR, FIND A NAME FOR HIM, AND HE WILL OBEY YOU!

AFTER THE BOY HAD CHRISTENED HIM "SHAZAM", THE HORSE ACCEPTED HIM AS HIS MASTER. THEN A NEW LIFE BEGAN FOR BARI, WHO COULD FINALLY EXPLORE THE GARDEN PARADISE OF THEIR NEW PLANET TO HIS HEART'S CONTENT...

RUN, SHAZAM! LEAP ACROSS THE CANYONS! WE'RE FLYING!

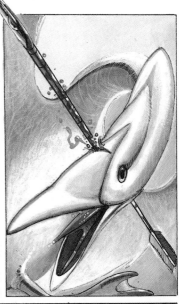

WELL DONE, FRIEND! TONIGHT, OTHON AND I WILL DINE ON THE ROASTED KARVIZ! YUM... AND FOR YOU, A BUSHEL OF OATS FROM ALDEBARAN!

FORGIVE ME, MASTER OTHON, BUT THE YOUNG BARI DID NOT GIVE ME THE CHANCE TO UNDRESS HIM. HE WAS SO EXHAUSTED THAT HE BARELY ATE BEFORE COLLAPSING INTO BED AND FALLING FAST ASLEEP...

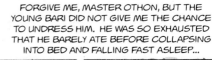

ZZZZZ...

I HAVE NEVER SEEN HIM SO HAPPY! BLESSED BE THE GREAT INVISIBLE!

EVEN I, MY GOOD IKU-TTA, FIND IT DIFFICULT TO ENDURE THE COLD LONELINESS OF MY BED. I LONG FOR A COMPANION...

TRUE, SHAZAM WAS A GODSEND. ESPECIALLY IN THIS SEASON, WITH THE MISTY NIGHTS THAT BRING DEPRESSION...

51

BASTARDS! THEY'VE TAKEN HIM! I'LL HUNT THEM DOWN AND KILL THEM ALL! IN ALL THIS FOG, THEY CAN'T HAVE GOTTEN FAR!

DON'T GO, MASTER! YOUR LEGS ARE STILL NOT STRONG ENOUGH! I'LL RUN AND ALERT YOUR FATHER, THE BARON!

NO ONE WILL GET MY HORSE BACK BUT ME! I CAN DEFEAT THEM EVEN WITHOUT MY LEGS. IN MY HEART, I HAVE ALREADY WON THE BATTLE!

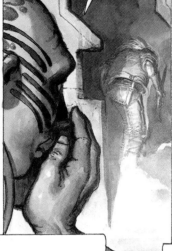

A THOUSAND PARDONS, MASTER OTHON... TERRIBLE TRAGE-DY... AND DANGER... THE HORSE IS STOLEN... YOUNG BARI HOT ON THE THIEVES' HEELS... IMPOSSIBLE TO STOP HIM! I REQUEST PERMISSION TO KILL MYSELF...

ENOUGH, IKU-TTA! NO MORE FOOLISHNESS! BRING MY ARMOR, QUICKLY!

FOUR MEN.... WITH SBR-17 SPIN-ACCELERATOR ARMOR... UNSURE OF THEIR STEPS... THEY'RE GETTING LOST IN THE FOG... THE TRACKS ARE FRESH... ONLY TEN MINUTES AHEAD OF US!

DON'T SOUND THE ALARM, IKU-TTA! WITH HIS CRIPPLED LEGS, BARI WILL NEVER BE ABLE TO CATCH THEM, AND I DON'T WANT ANYONE TO LEARN OF MY SON'S FAILURE. I'LL TAKE CARE OF IT... THE FOUR BANDITS WILL PAY FOR THEIR IMPUDENCE WITH THEIR LIVES!

53

54

56

THE BARON'S GROIN AND HIPS WERE OBLITERATED... IT WAS ONLY BECAUSE OF SHAZAM THAT HE WAS ABLE TO GET BACK TO HIS PALACE...

ATTENTIVE CARE FROM THE FAITHFUL IKU-TTA AND HIS TWO DAUGHTERS HELPED HIM RECOVER, AFTER SPENDING SEVERAL MONTHS CLOSE TO DEATH...

NOOO! IT WAS A PIRATE THAT I KILLED... NOT MY SON... BARI... ANSWER ME! COME BACK! DEATH IS ONLY AN ILLUSION... WE MUST WAKE UP!

A VERY RARE BIRD... OF SCARLET PLUMAGE... FELL TO THE EARTH... TO TURN INTO A FLOWER... THAT WILL GROW... AND GROW... HIGHER THAN THE SKY... YOUR SON WILL BE A RENOWNED WARRIOR... SLEEP... REST, MY LORD...

OTHON VON SALZA, TURNING HIS BACK ON PURE MARTIAL ARTS, INVESTED A LARGE PART OF HIS FABULOUS FORTUNE IN THE DEVELOPMENT OF THE FIRST METABARONIC WEAPONS...

AND ALSO BEGAN THE TRADITION OF CYBERNETIC IMPLANTS, BY INCORPORATING A MULTI-PROTONIC PELVIS...

JUST A MINUTE, TONTO! I MUST BE MISSING SOMETHING... LIFE FORMS DO NEED GENITALS TO REPRODUCE, RIGHT?

OF COURSE. PENIS, GONADS, SPERM...

WELL?! SINCE BARI DIED, HOW COULD THE CASTRATED OTHON VON SALZA HAVE ANOTHER SON? DID HE ADOPT AN ORPHAN TO CONTINUE HIS LINEAGE?

NO, LOTHAR! HE DIDN'T ADOPT. HE FATHERED A SON BY A WOMAN HE LOVED... A SON OF HIS OWN FLESH, OF HIS OWN BLOOD...

WHAT AN EXTRAORDINARY MARVEL! I THINK I'M GOING TO FRY ANOTHER DIODE... TELL ME QUICKLY... HOW DID HE DO IT?!

WE MUST GET DINNER READY. OUR MASTER THE METABARON SHOULD BE RETURNING SOON. I WILL TELL YOU ABOUT IT TOMORROW...

MEANIE!

JODOROWSKY JIMÉNEZ ©

A HARSH MAY WIND SWEEPS ACROSS THE SMOOTH TEFLO-CONCRETE SHELL OF EARTH, 2014...

CYBER-COPS STAND WATCH... IN VAIN, SINCE NO HUMAN SOUL HAS INHABITED THE CITY-SHAFT FOR OVER THREE CENTURIES...

A GUST OF WIND BEARS A ZACUDA FROLEX, THE LAST OF ITS KIND...

...DROPPING IT THROUGH ONE OF THE VENTILATION HATCHES...

...OF THE SORDID METAL PROTRUSION THAT IS POLICE CENTRAL.

IN ITS DEATH THROES, THE ZACUDA FROLEX FALLS BETWEEN THE KEYS OF THE BT-45891020354562 MINOR COMPUTER...

...BUT LAYS A SINGLE EGG BEFORE DYING...

THEN THE PERIOD OF ARTIFICIAL RAIN PASSES...

...BRINGING EVENINGS CAST IN RED BY A DYING SUN...

...ONE FINE DAY, THE EGG, HAVING ABSORBED G-SHOCKS FROM THE MACHINE, HATCHES...

...GIVING BIRTH TO AN ENORMOUS MUTANT ZACUDA FROLEX...

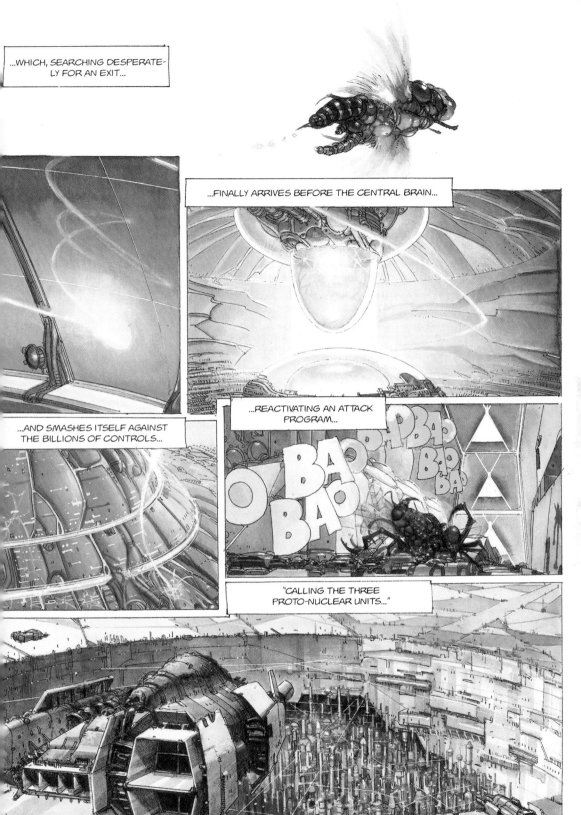

...WHICH, SEARCHING DESPERATE-LY FOR AN EXIT...

...FINALLY ARRIVES BEFORE THE CENTRAL BRAIN...

...AND SMASHES ITSELF AGAINST THE BILLIONS OF CONTROLS...

...REACTIVATING AN ATTACK PROGRAM...

"CALLING THE THREE PROTO-NUCLEAR UNITS..."

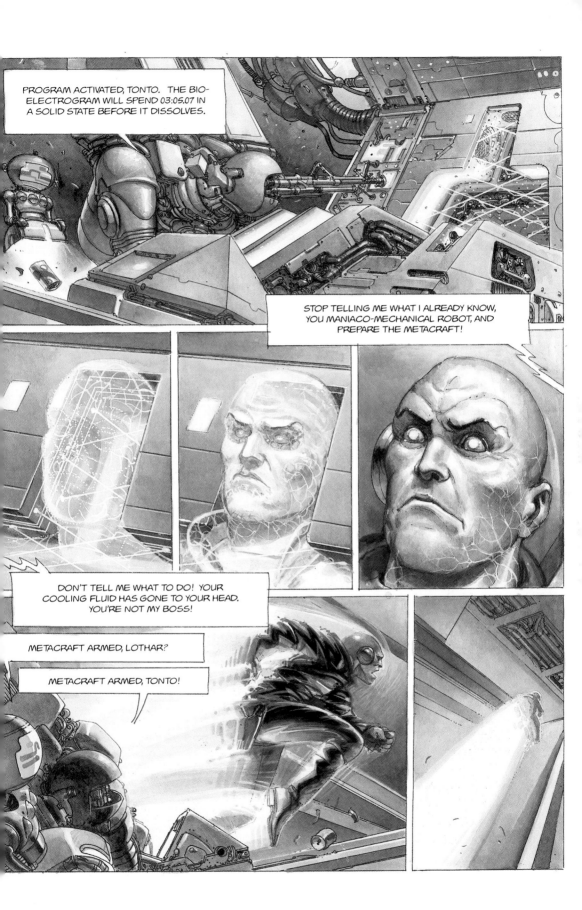

65

EXCELLENT, MASTER. SIMPLY SUPERB! VICTORY IS YOURS! I AM HONORED TO SERVE SUCH AN INVINCIBLE HUMAN WARRIOR!

OH!

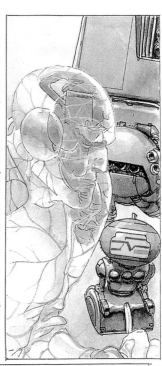

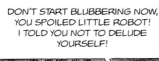

DON'T START BLUBBERING NOW, YOU SPOILED LITTLE ROBOT! I TOLD YOU NOT TO DELUDE YOURSELF!

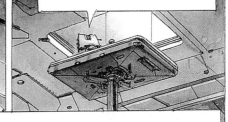

BUT WHERE HAS THE MASTER GONE? I MISS HIM SO MUCH! WITHOUT HIS BIO-HEAT, MY CIRCUITS WILL CORRODE... I'M AFRAID OF BECOMING MECHA-NICALLY PARALYZED!

IT'S SAD TO SEE YOU SUFFER SO MUCH FROM MERE BOREDOM... WOULD YOU LIKE ME TO CONTINUE THE STORY OF THE ORIGINS OF THE CLAN OF THE METABARONS?

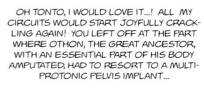

OH TONTO, I WOULD LOVE IT...! ALL MY CIRCUITS WOULD START JOYFULLY CRACK-LING AGAIN! YOU LEFT OFF AT THE PART WHERE OTHON, THE GREAT ANCESTOR, WITH AN ESSENTIAL PART OF HIS BODY AMPUTATED, HAD TO RESORT TO A MULTI-PROTONIC PELVIS IMPLANT...

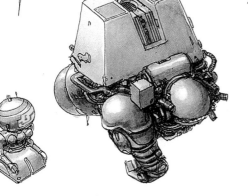

THAT'S RIGHT... AND YOU ASKED ME HOW THE NEXT METABARON WOULD BE CONCEI-VED IF OTHON HAD NO GENITALS...

YES, TONTO! I CAN'T WAIT TO FIND OUT! I'M ABOUT TO FRY ONE OF MY DIODES! HOW DID HE MANAGE TO HAVE A SON OF HIS OWN FLESH AND HIS OWN BLOOD?

67

HOLD ON! LET'S NOT GET AHEAD OF OURSELVES! I'LL BEGIN AT THE BEGINNING — ALL HUMAN ACTION IS TERRIBLY COMPLICATED AND EACH EVENT IS THE PRODUCT OF NUMEROUS CAUSES... YOU WILL SEE...

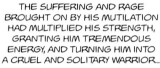

AS I TOLD YOU, OTHON VON SALZA (THE GREAT ANCESTOR OF THE CURRENT METABARON, OUR MASTER) TURNING HIS BACK ON PURE MARTIAL ARTS, INVESTED A LARGE PART OF HIS FABULOUS FORTUNE IN THE DEVELOPMENT AND CONSTRUCTION OF THE FIRST METABARONIC WEAPONS...

THE SUFFERING AND RAGE BROUGHT ON BY HIS MUTILATION HAD MULTIPLIED HIS STRENGTH, GRANTING HIM TREMENDOUS ENERGY, AND TURNING HIM INTO A CRUEL AND SOLITARY WARRIOR...

AND, ALTHOUGH HE STILL SLEPT WITH THE DAUGHTERS OF HIS FAITHFUL SLAVE IKU-TTA, WHO WERE AS LOYAL AS THE PALEO-DOGS OF ANCIENT TIMES, HE ALLOWED THEM THE RIGHT TO SATISFY EACH OTHER'S DESIRES AS LONG AS THEY NEVER SPOKE ANOTHER WORD...

WITH AN ARMY OF MACHINES, HE DEVASTATED THE NATURAL BEAUTY OF HIS PLANET OKHAR TO TRANSFORM THE RURAL CASTAKA FORTRESS INTO A MAXI-PROTONIC TOWER...

68

ON FOGGY NIGHTS, AFTER HIS USUAL SUPPER OF RAW LIZARDS, HE WOULD LISTEN TO THE NEWS OF THE GALAXY WHILE SIPPING A GLASS OF FINE WHISKY, SO AS NOT TO FORGET THE LANGUAGE OF HUMANS.

TODAY, AFTER THIRTY YEARS OF UNCEASING EFFORTS, THE HOSPITAL-PLANET HAS FINALLY ACHIEVED THE LONG-AWAITED MIRACLE FERTILIZATION OF ONE OF THE EMPRESS'S OVA BY THE EMPEROR'S STERILE SPERM. THIS DAY IS DECLARED A HOLIDAY ACROSS THE ENTIRE GALAXY!

WHAT FOOLS! THAT'S LIKE WAVING A BONE UNDER A DOG'S NOSE! THEY'LL AROUSE THE GREED OF ALL THE PIRATES...!

MY COGWHEELS ARE SPINNING WITH EXCITEMENT! OTHON VON SALZA WAS RIGHT: THE WHOLE GALAXY HAD BEEN WAITING FOR THE IMPERIAL COUPLE'S CHILD... THE FUTURE OF THE UNION OF PLANETS DEPENDED UPON ITS BIRTH...

THAT'S RIGHT! AND IF THE PIRATES GOT HOLD OF THE FETUS, THEY COULD DEMAND AN ENORMOUS RANSOM...

NOT SO FAST, TONTO... COULDN'T THE HOSPITAL-PLANET JUST MAKE ANOTHER ONE?

ROBO-NONSENSE! IT HAD TAKEN THEM 30 YEARS, 10 DAYS, 5 HOURS, AND 08:07.12 TO FERTILIZE THE OVUM WITH THE EMPEROR'S SPERM... IMMENSE FORTUNES HAD BEEN INVESTED IN THE UNDERTAKING...

THE PLANET HAD STOPPED TREATING THE SICK... IT KEPT THEM FROZEN IN THEIR SHIPS, WAITING FOR THE MIRACLE OF SCIENCE TO OCCUR...

UNTIL THE DAY WHEN, DUE TO AN INEXPLICABLE COINCIDENCE AND THE LABORS OF AN ENTIRE PLANET, THE IMPERIAL EMBRYO WAS CREATED. PERHAPS IT WOULD BE A SUPERIOR MUTANT...?

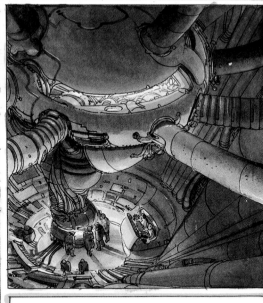

SIAMESE TWINS, MALE AND FEMALE, JOINED AT THE NECK AND SHOULDERS...

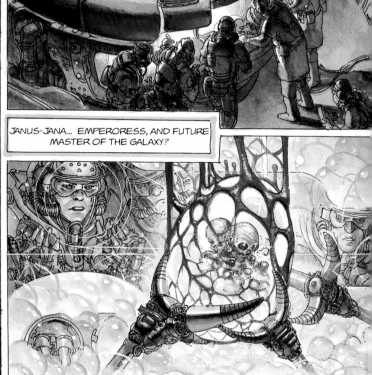

JANUS-JANA... EMPERORESS, AND FUTURE MASTER OF THE GALAXY?

IN ORDER TO TRANSPORT THE PERFECT ANDROGYNE FROM THE HOSPITAL-PLANET TO THE GOLDEN PLANET, HOME OF THE IMPERIAL COUPLE, A FORTRESS-SHIP, THE "MOTHER-COACH", WAS BUILT, AND ASSIGNED THE STRONGEST ESCORT OF PURPLE ENDOGUARDS THAT HAD EVER BEEN ASSEMBLED...

MY WIRES ARE TWISTING WITH IMPATIENCE! BIO-NUTS, GET ON WITH THE ATTACK! TELL ME NOW!

A PIRATE MEGA SPACECRAFT-CARRIER, DISGUISED AS A PLANET...

SILENCE YOUR VOCODER, YOU IGNORANT ROBOT UNPRO-GRAMED WITH GOOD MAN-NERS! JUST LISTEN!

71

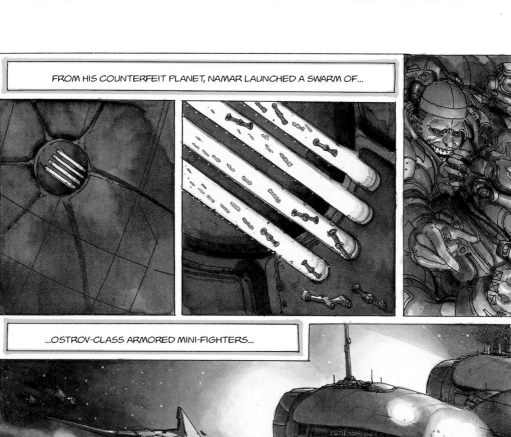

FROM HIS COUNTERFEIT PLANET, NAMAR LAUNCHED A SWARM OF...

...OSTROV-CLASS ARMORED MINI-FIGHTERS...

THE 100,000 KILLERS FLUNG THEMSELVES IN PURSUIT OF THE MOTHER-COACH...

THE STARS OF THE HARP CONSTELLATION PALED IN COMPARISON WITH THE BATTLE'S EXPLOSIONS...! EACH PURPLE LANCET HAD TO FACE A CLOUD OF BLOODTHIRSTY MOSQUITOES...

THE BATTLE THREATENED TO RAGE FOR MONTHS... THE EKONOMAT AND THE COLONIAL PLANETS REFRAINED FROM REQUESTING REINFORCEMENTS, WAITING FOR THE PIRATES TO WIN SO AS TO REPURCHASE THE PERFECT ANDROGYNE FROM THEM LATER, AND THEN SEIZE POWER...

BIO-CORRUPTION MAKES ME PUKE, BUT IT DOESN'T SURPRISE ME! HOW COULD BODIES DESIGNED TO ROT AND BE FOOD FOR WORMS EVER UNDERSTAND OUR SUPERIOR ROBOTIC INTEGRITY?

THE DISMAYED EMPEROR AND EMPRESS DECIDED TO MAKE A PUBLIC APPEAL TO THE CIVILIAN POPULATION FOR HELP...

ATTENTION PLEASE!

WORK AS HARD AS I DO, METALLIC DOGS! WITH ANGER, AND WITH RESENTMENT! THIS SHIP WILL MAKE UP FOR THE LOSS OF MY ORGAN! I WILL DEFEAT THEM ALL!

WHAT A MIRACLE! THE MASTER SPEAKS AGAIN...

ATTENTION TELE-BROADCASTERS THROUGHOUT THE GALAXY: AN URGENT MESSAGE LIVE FROM THE GOLDEN PLANET!

WE, YOUR IMPERIAL MAJESTIES, ISSUE AN URGENT APPEAL FOR HELP, INVITING ALL OUR SUBJECTS TO PARTICIPATE IN ELIMINATING THESE CONTEMPTIBLE PIRATES...

WHAT GOOD IS ALL THIS EXCITEMENT? ADVANCE TOO QUICKLY AND YOU CATCH UP WITH DEATH... ADVANCE TOO SLOWLY AND DEATH CATCHES UP WITH YOU!

BRING US YOUR IDEAS FOR WINNING THE BATTLE! ANY STRATEGY THAT ALLOWS US TO BRING AN END TO THIS STAND-OFF WILL BE MAGNIFI- CENTLY REWARDED!

WE DESPERATELY NEED ALL THE PEOPLE IN OUR VAST EMPIRE TO PROTECT THE SACRED EGG!

OUR CHILD... IS THE LINK THAT WILL UNITE ALL FAC- TIONS! THE MESSIAH OF REASON!

CIRCUITS COM- PLETE.

DEFENSES IN PLACE.

SCANNERS ACTI- VATED.

WEAPONS CHAR- GED.

PALEO-CHRIST! THE EMPIRE HAS BECOME NOTHING MORE THAN A SEETHING DEN OF TRAITORS. THE IMPERIAL COUPLE HAS BEEN FORCED TO CALL UPON THE HELP OF CIVILIANS... HOW HUMILIATING!

MY INSTINCT WILL GUIDE THIS SHIP...

I'LL SHOW THEM A THING OR TWO! THOSE "GREAT" WARRIORS ARE MORE IMPOTENT THAN I AM!

OTHON VON SALZA, EASILY DODGING THE POLY-RADARS, QUANTUM SEN- SORS AND PHOTONIC BARRIERS, ENTE- RED THE PURE OXYGEN ATMOSPHERE OF THE GOLDEN PLANET. SECURE IN ITS INVINCIBILITY, THE PLANET GLOWED LIKE A COLD SUN...

76

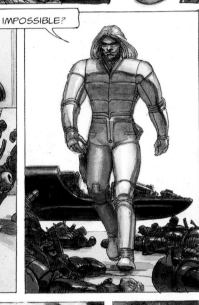

YOUR MAJESTIES, I AM THE ONE YOU'VE BEEN WAITING FOR!...

I'VE DEVELOPED A VERY SIMPLE PLAN THAT WILL ALLOW US TO WIPE OUT THE ENTIRE PIRATE FLEET WITHOUT THE LOSS OF A SINGLE SHIP...

THE IMPERIAL COUPLE, WON OVER BY OTHON'S SCANDALOUS ENTRANCE AND BY THE ASTONISHING CLEVERNESS OF HIS PLAN, IMMEDIATELY ENTRUSTED HIM WITH THE COMMAND OF THE 50 ENDOGUARD SHIPS STILL REMAINING ON THE GOLDEN PLANET.

50 IMPERIAL VESSELS AGAINST 100,000 PIRATE PREDATORS! INSANE! JUST IMAGINE! I CAN FEEL MY OIL STARTING TO OVERHEAT... I THINK I'M GOING TO FRY A DIODE...

WITH THE SMALL AND STRANGELY CAMOUFLAGED FLEET UNDER HIS COMMAND, OTHON VON SALZA DID NOT SET HIS SIGHTS UPON THE FORTRESS SHIP THAT HELD THE PERFECT ANDROGYNE, BUT OF COURSE UPON...

...THE MEGA-CARRIER, THE ROVING PIRATE HOME BASE, WHICH HE ATTACKED WITHOUT DELAY...

THEY'RE ATTACKING OUR BASE WITH TRI-H TORPEDOES! THAT'S ILLEGAL! IT'S DESPICABLE! THERE'S NO TIME TO LOSE! WE MUST CHASE THEM THROUGH THE ASTEROIDS!

ATTENTION ALL UNITS: ABORT DEFENSIVE MANEUVERS! HEAD FOR THE ASTEROIDS!

WE WILL PULVERIZE THESE UNSCRUPULOUS ATTACKERS!

AND, WHILE THE PREDATORS CONVERGED AMONG THE ASTEROIDS, THE 50 ENDOCRAFT SCATTERED, AS SILENTLY AS A FLOCK OF OWLS IN THE NIGHT...

...SETTING OFF THE FB3 BOMBS THAT THEY HAD HIDDEN WITHIN THE FISSURES OF THE ANCIENT ROCKS...

NOT A SINGLE PIRATE SURVIVED. THE FALSE PLANET WAS FORCED TO SURRENDER. THE UNFLAGGING OTHON ASKED THE EMPEROR FOR THE HONOR OF JOINING THE MOTHER-COACH'S ESCORT. THIS HONOR WAS GRANTED TO HIM...

SPECIAL PERMIT 6K975M325, BARON OTHON VON SALZA OF PLANET OKHAR IN THE DIAMOND CONSTELLATION. PLEASE CONFIRM...

PHEWWEE! PAUSE YOUR STORY THERE FOR A MOMENT, MY DIODES HAVE FINALLY FRIED! I'M GOING TO HAVE TO DRINK A DOUBLE DOSE OF ULTRA-COOLANT! WHAT AN ADVENTURE!

AFFIRMATIVE! TAKE YOUR PLACE AT THE REAR!

81

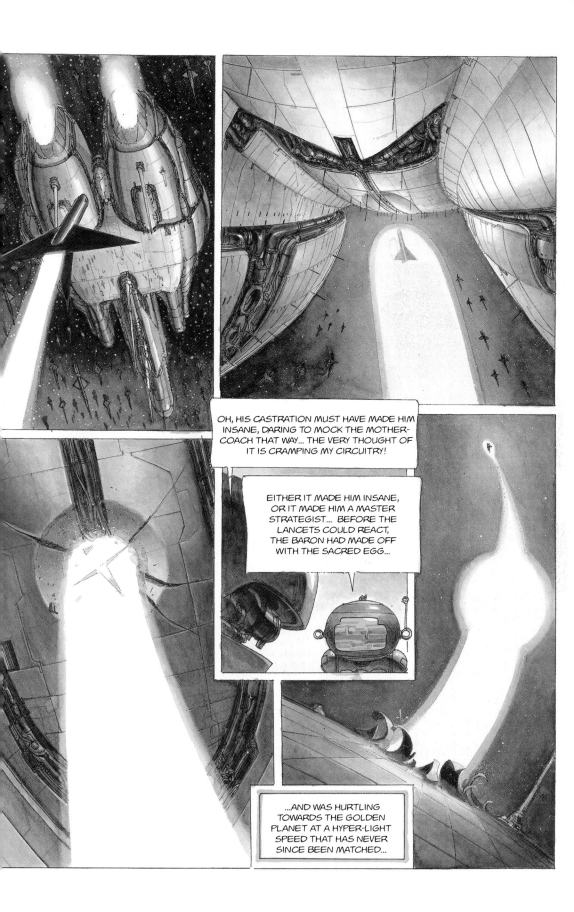

OH, HIS CASTRATION MUST HAVE MADE HIM INSANE, DARING TO MOCK THE MOTHER-COACH THAT WAY... THE VERY THOUGHT OF IT IS CRAMPING MY CIRCUITRY!

EITHER IT MADE HIM INSANE, OR IT MADE HIM A MASTER STRATEGIST... BEFORE THE LANCETS COULD REACT, THE BARON HAD MADE OFF WITH THE SACRED EGG...

...AND WAS HURTLING TOWARDS THE GOLDEN PLANET AT A HYPER-LIGHT SPEED THAT HAS NEVER SINCE BEEN MATCHED...

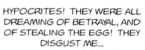

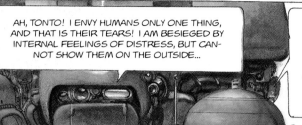

AH, TONTO! I ENVY HUMANS ONLY ONE THING, AND THAT IS THEIR TEARS! I AM BESIEGED BY INTERNAL FEELINGS OF DISTRESS, BUT CAN- NOT SHOW THEM ON THE OUTSIDE...

WHAT DO YOU EXPECT ME TO DO, LOTHAR? PRAISE YOUR EXQUISITE SENSITIVITY? YOU INCURABLY NAR- CISSISTIC MACHINE! HAVE YOU NEVER HEARD THAT FAMOUS SAYING BY THE FIRST IN THE LINE OF ARTIFICIAL BRAINS: "ALL THAT WHICH WE CALL 'DEAD IS LIABLE TO BE REBORN!" SILENCE YOUR INTERNAL CLAMORINGS, AND LISTEN...

ONE FINE SPRING EVENING, AS SWARMS OF WINGED CATS FLUTTERED TO AND FRO, GUZZLING THE NECTAR OF THE 'FLOWER THAT SINGS ONLY ONCE', AND WHILE OTHON, ON HIS OWN, RODE SHAZAM AS HE THOUGHT OF BARI, HIS DEAD SON...

...AN IMPERIAL VESSEL ARRIVED, BEARING THE PROMISED GIFT...

OTHON GALLOPED TOWARDS THE SHELTER OF HIS FORTRESS. HE REFUSED TO FACE ANY MORE DISAPPOINTMENTS...

...AND HE SHUT HIMSELF UP IN HIS GREAT HALL OF WEAPONS.

I ORDER THAT THOSE DOORS MAY NOT BE OPENED FOR ANY REA- SON! I WILL RECEIVE NO ONE!

VERY WELL, MASTER.

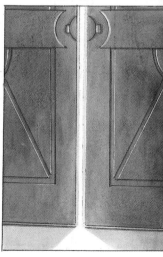

THAT VERY NIGHT THERE WAS
AN ECLIPSE OF THE MOON...
BILLIONS OF PROTOGLOW-WORMS
PERFORMED A FRANTIC MATING
DANCE THAT LIT UP THE DARKNESS...

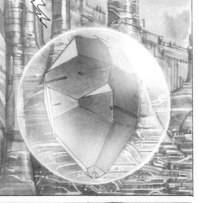

ENOUGH, TONTO! TAKE YOUR POETIC COMMENTARIES
AND SHOVE THEM UP YOUR DRAINAGE VALVE!
HURRY AND TELL ME THE REST, MY ELECTRO-SYNOVIAL FLUID
IS STARTING TO BOIL...! DID THE GREAT ANCESTOR FALL IN LOVE?

MADLY IN LOVE...
BUT...

YOU SEE, HONORATA...
OUR UNION IS IMPOSSIBLE... DESTINY
HAS MADE A MOCKERY OF ME...

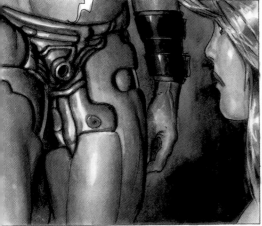

91

HOORAY! AND SHE GAVE HIM A BEAUTIFUL CHILD, AND THEY LIVED HAPPILY EVER AFTER, AND SO THE CLAN OF THE METABARONS WOULD LIVE ON!

STOP HOPPING AROUND MADLY LIKE A HUMAN HOOKED ON SILO-PHETAMINES, LOTHAR... IT'S NOT A FAIRY TALE I'M TELLING, YOU KNOW!

THE BIRTH WAS A TRAGIC EVENT, AND WAS TO DISRUPT THE CHILD'S WHOLE EXISTENCE... HAVE YOUR SYSTEM RELEASE SOME CALMING FLUID, THEN OPEN YOUR AUDITORY CHANNELS...

ONE PEACEFUL MORNING IN THE NINTH MONTH OF PREGNANCY, WHILE, AS USUAL, OTHON WAS OUT WITH SHAZAM...

MASTER, MASTER! YOU MUST RETURN TO THE TOWER IMMEDIATELY!

IT ANGERS ME THAT I MUST BRING YOU DESPAIR AT THE PRECISE MOMENT WHEN YOUR HEART IS FULL OF JOY... HOWEVER, IT IS IN THE NATURE OF THINGS THAT FLOWERS FADE, AND THAT...

HUFF! HUFF!

HMM... WHAT'S HAP-PENING, IKU-TTA?

SPEAK! GET TO THE FACTS! SPARE ME THE CONVOLUTED METAPHORS OF YOUR KIND!

HE WHO GIVES LIFE IS TIRED, HIS HEART IS FULL OF DISGUST, AND HE INTENDS THE ANNIHILA-TION OF YOUR WIFE AND MY TWO DAUGHTERS...

WHAT ARE YOU SAYING, YOU WRETCHED MAN?

JEALOUSY, MASTER! MY DAUGHTERS HAVE SEIZED LADY HONORATA AND NOW DESIRE, BEFORE THROWING THEMSELVES WITH HER FROM THE TOP OF YOUR TOWER THAT YOU HEAR THEIR FINAL WORDS OF LOVE...

PALEO-CHRIST!

95

97

OTHON, I LOVE YOU!

99

SO AS TO PROCLAIM IT THE PERFECT ANDROGYNE, USING IT TO GAIN THE COMBINED SUPPORT OF THE MAJORITY OF THE PLANETS, THEN TAKE OVER THE THRONE, AFTER POISONING JANUS-JANA...

WHAT A DASTARDLY PLAN!

WHICH WAS COMPLETELY RUINED BY MY FALLING IN LOVE WITH YOU... I DISOBEYED THE ORDERS OF THE SHABDA-OUD, AND GAVE BIRTH TO A BOY WHO WILL ALLOW THE CLAN OF THE METABARONS TO LIVE ON, AS YOU INTENDED.

SO WHAT WILL HAPPEN NOW?

IN ACCORDANCE WITH OUR LAW, AND TO PREVENT ANY RISK OF SCANDAL, THEY WOULD BE FORCED TO ASSASSINATE US BOTH, THE CHILD AND ME...

THEN THEY WILL NEVER LEARN THAT THE CHILD IS A BOY!

IF I STICK TO THE PLAN, I AM SUPPOSED TO KIDNAP THE CHILD WHEN HE TURNS SEVEN YEARS OLD AND BRING HIM TO THEM...

VERY WELL. WE'LL KEEP THE SECRET TO OURSELVES FOR AT LEAST THOSE SEVEN YEARS! THAT WILL GIVE US TIME TO PLAN OUR DEFENSE AND MAKE A WARRIOR OF MY SON...

OUR TIME IS VERY SHORT: THE TIME WE KNOW ONE ANOTHER. IN THIS LIFE, OUR EXISTENCE IS ONLY SOMETHING THAT WE LOAN BETWEEN US.

WE SHALL ALL DISAPPEAR. NOTHING WILL REMAIN OF US... COVERED IN FLOWERS, WE MUST LEAVE THIS WORLD...

OUR HOME IS NOT OF THIS WORLD. WE FIND OUR TRUE HOME WHERE THOSE WITHOUT BODIES DWELL...

WITH OUR MOST BEAUTIFUL SONGS LET US ACCOMPANY THE TRAVELERS WHO NOW RETURN TOWARDS THEIR TRUE DOMICILE...

WAIT HERE FOR ME A MOMENT...

SO IKU-TTA COMMITTED SUICIDE. BETTER THAT WAY. HIS PRESENCE WILL NO LONGER BE A THREAT TO THE CHILD...

STOP! THIS INCIDENT WAS UNPARDONABLE! FROM NOW ON, UNDER PENALTY OF DEATH, ENTRY TO MY FORTRESS WILL BE FORBIDDEN TO ALL MEMBERS OF THE TRIBE. MY ROBOTS WILL TEND TO MY DOMESTIC NEEDS. I HAVE SPOKEN...!

WE SHALL NAME HIM AGHNAR...

YES, OTHON. AGHNAR HAS FED WELL. NOW HE MUST SLEEP...

104

ALL RIGHT. BUT I WISH TO HEAR NOTHING OF THE CHILD DURING THE NEXT SEVEN YEARS...

AT THAT TIME, I WILL PUT HIM TO THE TEST OF WARRIORHOOD. IF HE SURVIVES, I WILL ALLOW HIM TO SUCCEED ME...

AND IF NOT?

HE WILL DIE... AND THAT WILL BE THE END OF OUR CLAN... FOR I WILL KILL MYSELF AS WELL...

OHMY-OHMY-OHMY! THIS TIME I'M NOT JUST GOING TO FRY MY DIODES BUT ALSO THE AUDIO-GYROSCOPES THAT ENABLE ME TO WALK! MY CATHODES ARE MELTING WITH CURIOSITY! HOW WILL A WEIGHTLESS CHILD BECOME THE BEST WARRIOR IN THE GALAXY? WHAT WILL HIS INITIATION BE LIKE? WILL HONORATA WITHSTAND SEVEN LONG YEARS OF SEPARATION FROM OTHON WITHOUT DIMINISHING HER LOVE?

SHUT YOUR RUSTY OLD TRAP! YOU'RE MORE INQUISITIVE THAN A HAIRDRESSER ON TERRA PRIMA!

TELL ME! TELL ME!

OK, I GET IT... BUT I CAN TELL YOU VERY LITTLE ABOUT THOSE SEVEN YEARS

HONORATA RODE SHAZAM TO ANASIRMA, THE SACRED MOUNTAIN...

A FORBIDDEN PLACE, LITTERED WITH DEADLY CHASMS. EVEN THE NATIVES HAD NOT VENTURED THERE FOR CENTURIES...

FLEEING AN ATTACK OF CARNIVOROUS EODACTYLS,
SHE TOOK SHELTER...

...IN THE CAVE OF SOFT CRYSTALS, WHICH CONSTANTLY EMIT A PERPETUAL WHISPER OF RUNNING WATER, AND ARE ALWAYS CHANGING FORMS...

SHE AND HER SON FED ON THE FLESH OF WOOLLY TOADS WHICH ENTERED THE CAVE DURING THE BITTER-COLD NIGHTS, SEEKING HUMAN WARMTH...

APPARENTLY, AGHNAR HAD TAKEN A LIKING TO ONE OF THESE CREATURES... A LARGE MALE, WHICH HAD MANAGED TO PICK UP A FEW DOZEN WORDS FROM HIM...

GO ON, YIPPI... SAY SOMETHING TO ME...

GIVE YIPPI HEAT... FROM BODY... YOU, MASTER... MY LORD... THANK YOU...

WHEN HER SON TURNED FIVE YEARS OLD, HONORATA ORDERED HIM TO CUT HIS FRIEND IN TWO. HE HAD TO LEARN TO CONTROL THE GRIEF HE WOULD FEEL. FOR EACH TEAR HE SHED, HE WOULD RECEIVE A LASH OF THE WHIP...

WHY, MASTER?

DUTY COMES BEFORE LOVE, YIPPI.

109

AGHNAR RECEIVED ONE LASH AND ONE LASH ONLY FROM HIS MOTHER FOR THE SINGLE TEAR HE SHED. A LASH WHICH LEFT A MARK ON HIM THAT WOULD NEVER BE ERASED...

USING SHABDA-OUD MEDITATION TECHNIQUES, AGHNAR LEARNED SUCH SELF-CONTROL OVER HIS NERVOUS SYSTEM THAT, BY AUTO-HYPNOSIS, HE WAS ABLE TO FREE HIS BODY FROM THE TYRANNY OF PAIN...

EACH TIME HE LET HIS ATTENTION WANDER, HE RECEIVED A BLOW...

THE CHILD REACHED ADULTHOOD VERY QUICKLY. HE COULD LOOK DEATH IN THE FACE AS WELL AS LIFE.

THAT'S THE SECOND TIME I'VE HAD TO WARN YOU THIS WEEK!

I KNOW, I KNOW... I MUST TRUST NO ONE, NOT EVEN MY OWN MOTHER...

¡SHAF!

110

EVERY SIX MONTHS, SHE WOULD ADD MORE WEIGHT TO HIM...

AND EVERY DAY, HE HAD TO FIGHT HIS MOTHER, WHO POSSESSED AMAZING STRENGTH. THEY FOUGHT FOR HOURS ON END.

DEFEND YOURSELF BETTER THAN THAT... AND ATTACK MORE VICIOUSLY...

ARRGH! I LOATHE EVERY ONE OF YOUR BLOWS! I SWEAR I'LL MAKE YOU TASTE THE DIRT!

THE CHILD'S ENERGY INCREASED DAY BY DAY...

...AND ONE FINE MORNING, DODGING THE HYPNOTIC WAVES SHE EMANATED, HE FINALLY MANAGED TO BEAT HIS MOTHER...

DO YOU GIVE IN?

I GIVE IN...

AND SHE GAVE HIM THE ONLY KISS HE RECEIVED IN HIS ENTIRE CHILDHOOD...

AS SHE FELT HIM PUT HIS YOUNG, ADORING LIPS TO HERS, HONORATA EXPERIENCED A MOMENT OF WEAKNESS AND LET HER TEARS FLOW, FOR ONE INSTANT CEASING TO BE HIS MERCILESS TRAINER, AND BECOMING SIMPLY HIS MOTHER...

HOW I TOO WOULD LOVE TO SIGH AND CRY AND GIVE BIRTH, SO THAT I WOULD KNOW WHAT A HUMAN MOTHER KNOWS! IT'S SO TOUCHING!

WHY NOT SMEAR YOUR DRAINAGE VALVE WITH RED PAINT EVERY 28 DAYS SO YOU CAN KNOW THE PLEASURE OF MENSTRUATION WHILE YOU'RE AT IT? YOU MECHANICAL FOOL... CEASE YOUR DIGRESSIONS, AND LISTEN...

BUT SHE RECOVERED VERY QUICKLY, AND HER SEVERITY SOON DRIED HER TEARS...

ENOUGH EMOTION. YOU MUST SHUT YOURSELF OFF FROM FEELING. NEVER FORGET THAT YOU ARE A CASTAKA...

TOMORROW YOU WILL TURN SEVEN YEARS OLD AND I WISH TO INTRODUCE YOU TO YOUR FATHER AS A WARRIOR WHO IS WORTHY...

...OF THE CLAN OF THE METABARONS...

DAWN HAD HARDLY BROKEN AS HONORATA AND AGHNAR, RIDING A TRAINED EODACTYL, REACHED THE CASTAKA FORTRESS.

THE SEVEN YEARS OF SEPARATION HAD TAKEN NOTHING AWAY FROM THE LOVE SHARED BY THOSE TWO EXTRAORDINARY BEINGS...

AND NOW IT'S YOU WHO'S LETTING YOUR POETIC ENTHUSIASM GET THE BETTER OF YOU, TONTO. BE VERY CAREFUL... YOU MIGHT FRY YOUR DIODES TOO...

OTHON!

HONORATA!

I SWEAR IN THE NAME OF THAT MENTAL CONSTRUCT WHICH HUMANS CALL "GOD", LOTHAR, IF YOU DARE INTERRUPT ME ONCE MORE, I WILL STOP TELLING MY STORY FOR GOOD. SAY YOU'RE SORRY TEN TIMES...

SORRY, SORRY, SORRY, SORRY, SORRY, SORRY, SORRY, SORRY, SORRY, SORRY, TONTO. NOW, PLEASE CONTINUE...

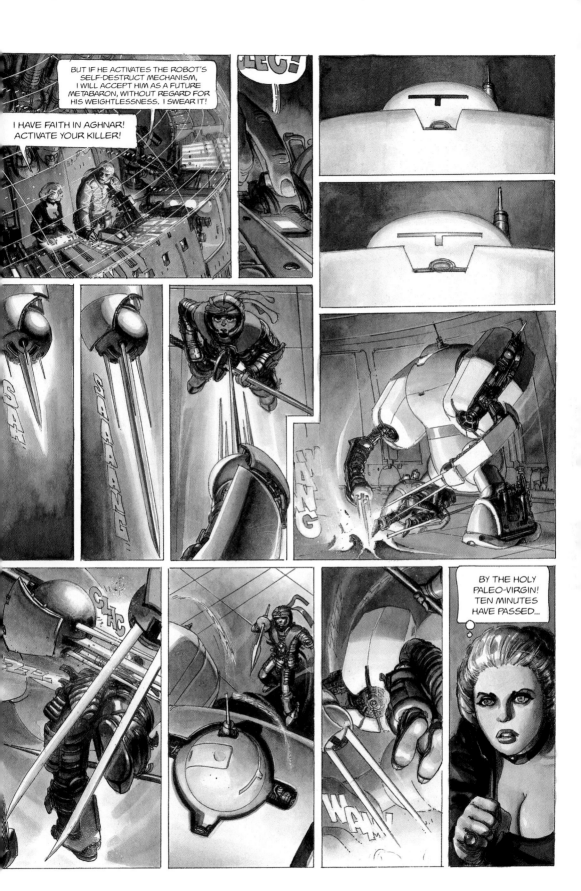

115

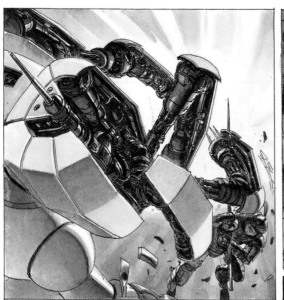

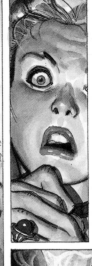

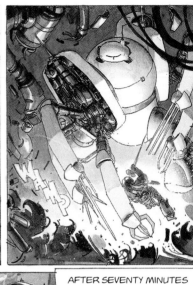

MY OIL IS BOILING! HAVE MERCY ON ME AND CUT IT SHORT, TONTO! HOW MANY ARMS DID THE ROBOT FINALLY GROW?

AFTER SEVENTY MINUTES AND THREE SECONDS OF DESPERATE BATTLE, THE KILLER FELL UPON THE CHILD WITH ITS EIGHT POWERFUL ARMS...

BY THE SACRED ULTRA-COOLANT THAT LUBRI-CATES THE CENTRAL BRAIN! A MECHANICAL SPIDER! AFTER MORE THAN AN HOUR'S FIGHTING, THE BOY MUST HAVE BEEN AT THE END OF HIS STRENGTH...

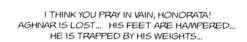

OH, MOST HOLY PALEO-VIRGIN, INSPIRE MY SON! LET HIM GO BEYOND THE LIMITS OF LOGIC! LET HIM IMPROVISE! I BEG YOU! HE WILL NEVER HIT THE RED BUTTON IN NORMAL COMBAT...

I THINK YOU PRAY IN VAIN, HONORATA! AGHNAR IS LOST... HIS FEET ARE HAMPERED... HE IS TRAPPED BY HIS WEIGHTS...

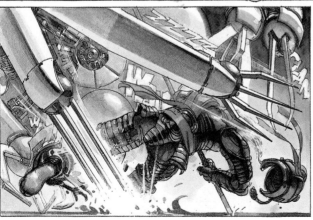

118

119

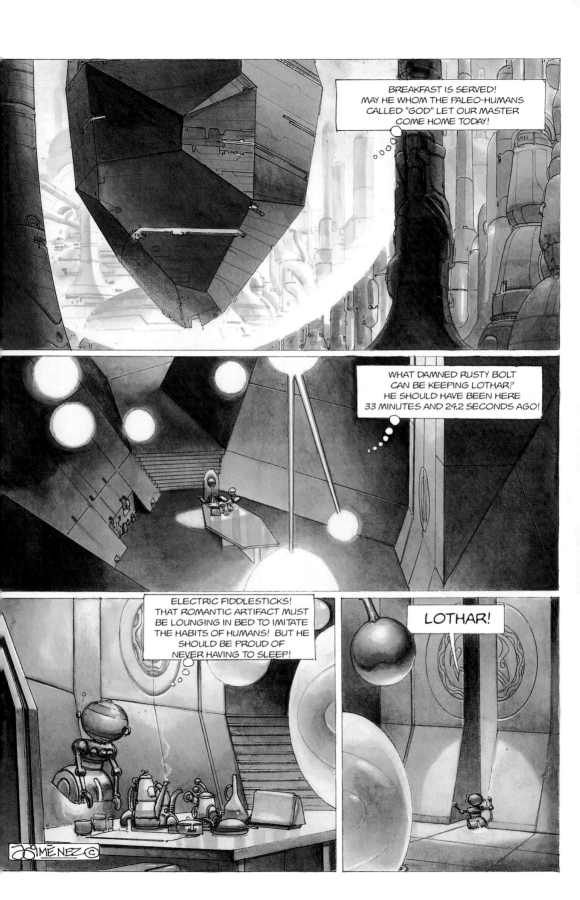

121

THIS IS CRAZY! THE MASTER IS SLICING THE METABUNKER IN HALF!

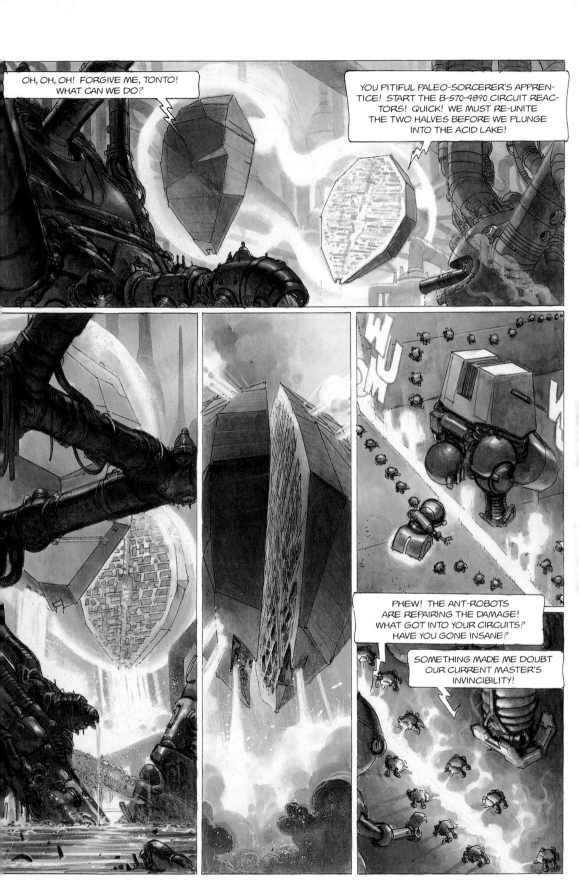

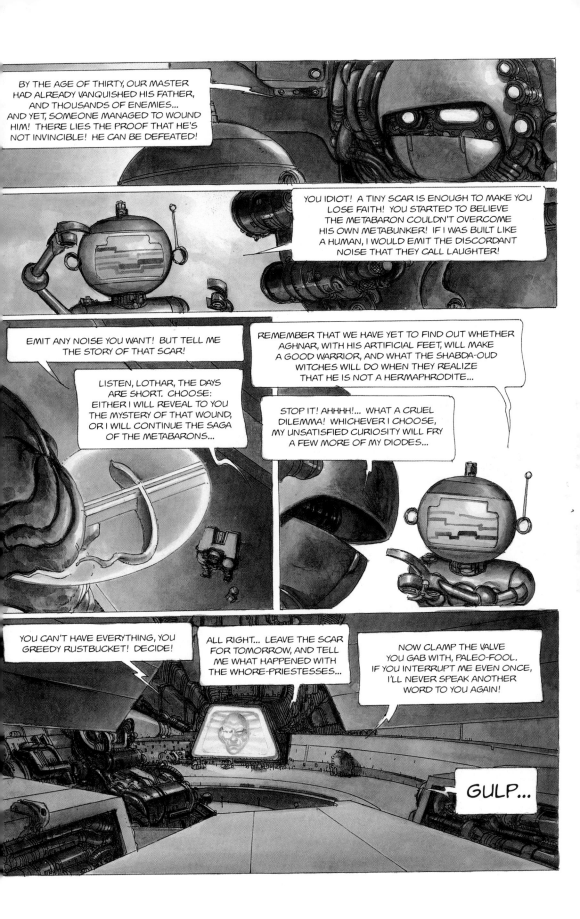

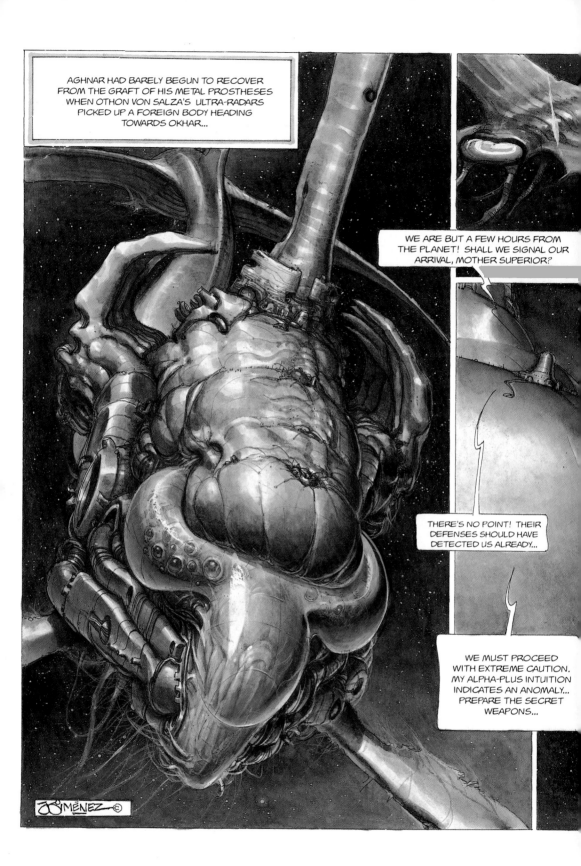

AGHNAR HAD BARELY BEGUN TO RECOVER FROM THE GRAFT OF HIS METAL PROSTHESES WHEN OTHON VON SALZA'S ULTRA-RADARS PICKED UP A FOREIGN BODY HEADING TOWARDS OKHAR...

WE ARE BUT A FEW HOURS FROM THE PLANET! SHALL WE SIGNAL OUR ARRIVAL, MOTHER SUPERIOR?

THERE'S NO POINT! THEIR DEFENSES SHOULD HAVE DETECTED US ALREADY...

WE MUST PROCEED WITH EXTREME CAUTION. MY ALPHA-PLUS INTUITION INDICATES AN ANOMALY... PREPARE THE SECRET WEAPONS...

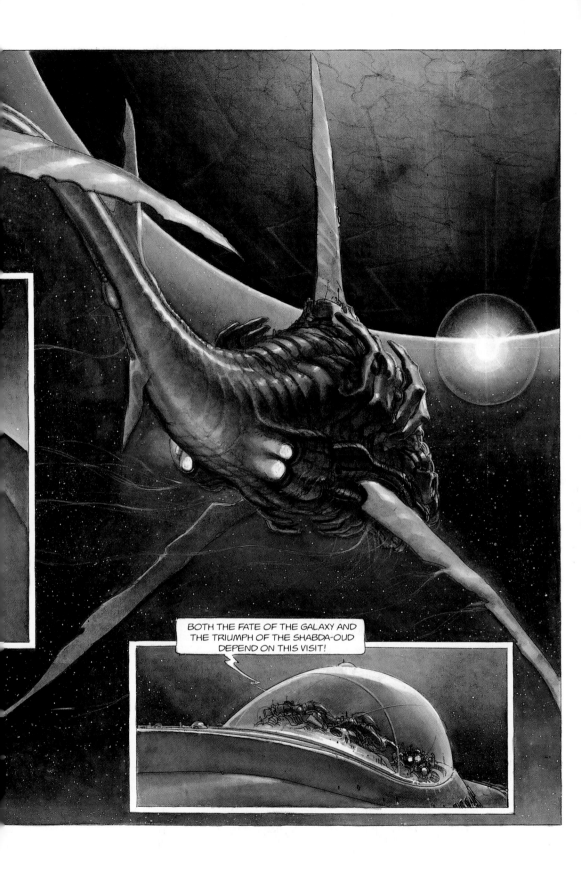

129

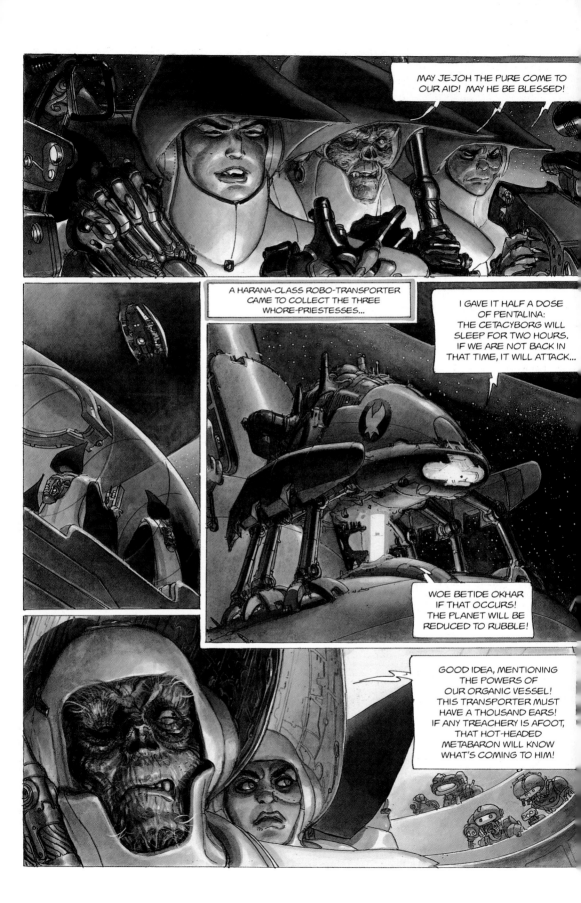

131

OTHON VON SALZA, SPARE US YOUR CEREMONIES! WE HAVE LITTLE TIME. THE OBJECT OF OUR VISIT CONFORMS TO CONVENT REGULATIONS. WE MUST BE ASSURED OF OUR PROTÉGÉE'S FAITH.

WOULD YOU BE GOOD ENOUGH TO PROVIDE US WITH A SECLUDED PLACE WHERE WE MIGHT EXAMINE YOUR WIFE?

OUR PSYCHO-TOUCH DETECTS NO HIDDEN MICROPHONES...

COMPLETELY SOUNDPROOF... NO HIDDEN WEAPONS...

THE LOCK CANNOT BE OPENED FROM OUTSIDE... THERE IS COMPLETE SECURITY... THE MOTHER SUPERIOR CAN SPEAK OPENLY...

NOT ONLY YOUR OWN EXISTENCE, BUT ALSO THAT OF THIS WHOLE PLANET DEPENDS ON YOUR ANSWERS...

I UNDERSTAND, MOTHER!

YOU WERE ORDERED TO CONCEIVE A HERMAPHRODITE, TO MAKE A PERFECT ANDROGYNE WHO WOULD BE PROCLAIMED EMPERORESS OF THE GALAXY! HE IS NOW SEVEN YEARS OLD – YOU SHOULD HAVE SENT HIM TO US. WHY HAVE YOU NOT DONE THIS?

I OBEYED THE ORDER. I BEGOT THE HERMAPHRODITE, BUT AT THE TIME I WAS TO GIVE HIM TO YOU, HIS FEET BECAME INFECTED BY POISONOUS BRAMBLES...

...AND WE HAD TO AMPUTATE THEM... HE HAS NOT YET ENTIRELY RECOVERED...

UNFORGIVABLE NEGLIGENCE!

THE PERFECT ANDROGYNE, A USELESS CRIPPLE!

YOU DESERVE A THOUSAND DEATHS, HONORATA!

JUST A MOMENT! LET ME FINISH! WE GRAFTED METALLIC PROSTHESES ONTO HIM, WHICH SERVE HIM BETTER THAN HUMAN FEET!

AGHNAR IS THE DIVINE HERMAPHRODITE! AS SOON AS HE CAN TRAVEL, I WILL BRING HIM TO YOU!

WE SHALL SEE IF YOU SPEAK THE TRUTH! BRING US YOUR SON!

I DON'T UNDERSTAND THIS AT ALL! AGHNAR IS COMPLETELY MALE! WHAT'S GOING TO HAPPEN? SURELY HONORATA WOULDN'T SEND HER SON TO BE RIPPED TO PIECES BY THOSE KILLERS!

SORRY, TONTO!

STOP STINKING UP YOUR FUSEBOX! I HOPE YOUR SYNOVIAL FLUID ROTS! I ASKED YOU NOT TO INTERRUPT! IF YOU WANT ME TO CONTINUE, SAY YOU'RE SORRY TWENTY TIMES!

133

ONLY A MINUTE HAD PASSED SINCE AGHNAR HAD ENTERED THE HALL OF ARMS FOR HIS EXAMINATION BY THE THREE PRIESTESSES... AND ALREADY HONORATA WAS TREMBLING ALL OVER...

...OUR SON WILL EMERGE VICTORIOUS FROM THIS TEST! REMEMBER, HE IS A CASTAKA!

DON'T LET YOUR MATERNAL INSTINCT CLOUD YOUR WARRIOR'S SPIRIT. APPLY THE TEACHING: "YOUR MIND EMPTY OF CONFUSION, YOUR HEART EMPTY OF WORRY, YOUR BELLY EMPTY OF FEAR..."

BUT I CAN'T HELP REMEMBERING THAT HE'S ONLY A CHILD! HE'S ONLY JUST GETTING OVER THE PAIN OF THE OPERATION! HE'S STILL LEARNING THE USE OF HIS NEW FEET...

...AND THE WHORE-PRIESTESSES ARE KILLERS OF THE WORST KIND! I TREMBLE FOR HIM!

ABSOLUTE ACCEPTANCE OF DEATH IS THE WARRIOR'S WAY!

HE IS CARRYING NO WEAPONS, EITHER UPON HIM OR WITHIN HIS BODY...

HIS BRAIN IS IN ALPHA-MODE... NO KILLER PROGRAMING...

GOOD. APPROACH, CHILD!

135

137

IT'S IMMENSE! I WILL PENETRATE ITS HULL NOW, WHILE IT SLEEPS!

139

140

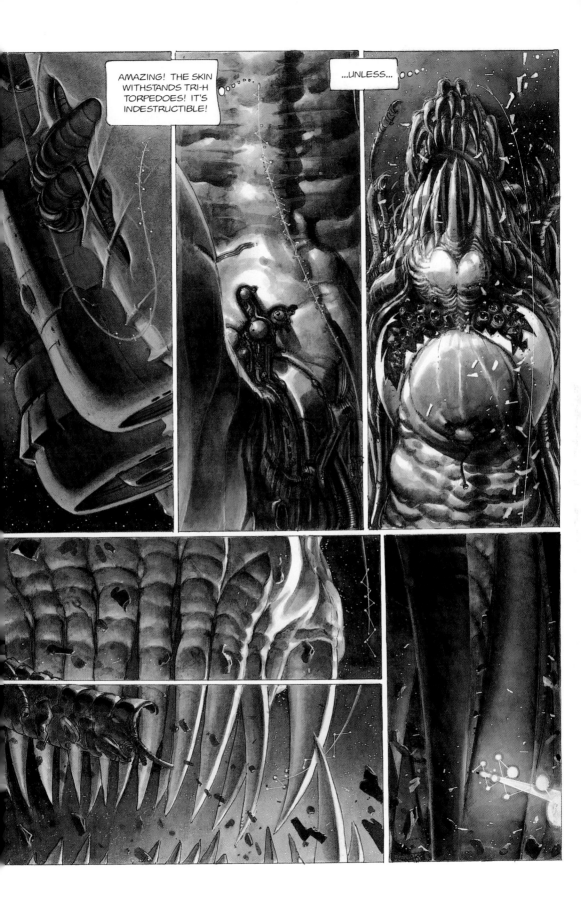

WHEN OTHON LAUNCHED
ALL HIS WEAPONS AT
ITS SERVO-BRAIN, THE
CETACYBORG EXPLODED
LIKE A SUPERNOVA.

MY SON, BY OVERCOMING THOSE THREE WITCHES, YOU PROVED YOU ARE A GREAT WARRIOR! SO YOU SHOULD UNDERSTAND ME!

A WARRIOR'S POWER IS LIKE WATER; IT ADAPTS TO ALL THAT IT ENCOUNTERS. JUST AS HE WHO DESIRES NOTHING NEVER FAILS, HE WHO WINS NOTHING, LOSES NOTHING. BY SLIPPING AWAY, A TRUE HERO ASSERTS HIMSELF.

THE CLAN OF THE METABARONS WILL CONTINUE TO THRIVE IN SECRET! AND WE WILL RE-EMERGE A FEW YEARS FROM NOW!

I UNDERSTAND, FATHER: HE WHO RENOUNCES GLORY IS A HERO TOO!

THEY WENT TO THE EMBARKATION PLATFORM WHERE THE METABUNKER AWAITED THEM... THE PERFECT WAR MACHINE, DESIGNED BY OTHON, WHO ALSO MADE THE PERFECT ROBOT, WHICH, IN ALL HUMILITY, IS ME...

PLEASE, SPARE ME YOUR WORDS OF SELF-PRAISE AND QUICKLY TELL ME THE REST! I'M SURE THEY WILL BE ATTACKED BY THE PRIESTESSES BEFORE THEY EVEN GET ON BOARD AND THAT, AS AGHNAR WAS HOPING, THEY WILL BE FORCED TO RETALIATE!

YOU HAVE NO IMAGINATION, YOU SQUAWKING SCRAP-HEAP! WHAT HAPPENED NEXT WAS INFINITELY MORE HORRIBLE!

TELL ME! TELL ME, OR I'LL PISS AWAY ALL MY OIL!

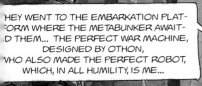

THE LAST TRUNKS AND THE METACRAFT WERE ALREADY BEING LOADED INTO THE METABUNKER. THE NATIVES WERE CHANTING SONGS OF FAREWELL... I WAS JUST PREPARING FOR TAKE-OFF, WHEN...

FAREWELL! FAREWELL! IT IS NORMAL FOR ALL OF US TO DEPART... WE COME HERE ONLY TO SLEEP... WE COME HERE ONLY TO DREAM... IT IS NOT TRUE, IT IS NOT TRUE THAT ALL OF US LIVE ON THIS EARTH!

WELCOME, MASTER!

...HONORATA UTTERED A FEW STRANGE WORDS...

147

SUCH A PROFOUNDLY HUMAN TRAGEDY! JUST THE THOUGHT OF HONORATA'S BODY DISINTEGRATING INTO A TORRENT OF FLESH HAS FRIED FOUR MORE OF MY DIODES! OOOOOOOOO!

STOP YOUR EFFEMINATE BLEATING! YOU'RE SPLITTING MY MECHADRUMS! I'M SICK OF ALL THESE INTERRUPTIONS AND YOUR DIODES FRYING ALL THE TIME...! COME HERE!

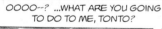

OOOO--? ...WHAT ARE YOU GOING TO DO TO ME, TONTO?

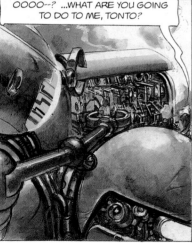

I AM REMOVING YOUR VERBAL MEMORY PLATE AND YOUR ERSATZ-EMOTION PLUG...

AND NOW, YOU USELESS SCRAP-HEAP, YOU CANNOT SPEAK, OR FRY ANY OF YOUR DIODES. NOW LISTEN...

Cover Gallery

ISSUES 1 THROUGH 5

REINVENTING THE METABARON

When Juan Gimenez first signed on to illustrate the stories of Alexandro Jodorowsky's ultimate warrior, the artist had to begin with an examination of the work Moebius had done before him. Beyond the Metabaron's role in The Incal, Moebius had also drawn a short origins story for the character: the perfect starting point for the Metabaron's own series.

Here now is a page by page comparison between the original layout done by Moebius and the pages done by Juan Gimenez.

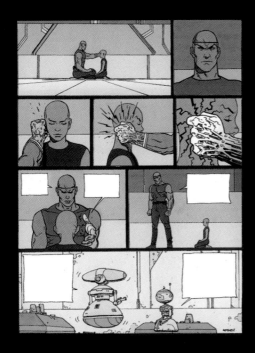

Juan Gimenez at his drawing board

JODOROWSKY

Alexandro Jodorowsky is born in Chile in 1929. He traverses Chile far and wide with a traveling puppet theater before departing for France in 1953 with 50 dollars in his pocket. In Paris, he creates numerous pantomimes for the mime Marcel Marceau, directs musical extravaganzas and spends his time with the surrealists, with whom he parts company in 1962 by founding the counter-cultural 'Panic movement' with Topor and Arrabal.

In 1965, Alexandro Jodorowsky returns to South America. In Mexico, he creates Mexico's avant-garde theater movement, and makes a name for himself in the cinema. First he adapts his friend Arrabal's play, FANDO & LYS, then shoots EL TOPO and THE HOLY MOUNTAIN.

In 1975, he begins work on a colossal project: adapting Frank Herbert's novel DUNE for the screen. He engages numerous design artists, such as H.R. Giger, Christopher Foss, and Mœbius to draw the storyboards, and offers the role of The Emperor to Salvador Dali. The film will finally be shot much later by David Lynch. Out of this disappointment comes a new duo to hit comic books; in 1978, Mœbius and Jodorowsky complete their first collaboration, an illustrated fable: THE EYES OF THE CAT. In 1980, the two men embark upon the subsequently legendary series, THE INCAL.

Alexandro Jodorowsky has now become one of the most eminent comic book authors in Europe. He enjoys success after success in collaboration with all the best-known artists.

His novels and poems are published all over the world. Alexandro Jodorowsky is also a great expert of the Tarot.

GIMENEZ

Juan Gimenez is born in Mendoza, Argentina, in 1943. As a young man, he studies precision engineering and industrial design. He publishes his first comic at the age of sixteen. After a long hiatus, during which he spends his time most notably on promotional films, he returns to comic books. He draws regularly for editors of Spanish and Italian magazines, then illustrates a number of comic books in France.

In 1981, he works on an episode in Gerard Potterton's American animated film, HEAVY METAL. The saga of the Metabarons started to be published in Europe in 1992. It continues to be published there, where the series is meeting with ever more resounding success.

His comic book work aside, Juan Gimenez is also a prolific illustrator, whose work can be seen on book jackets, album covers, posters, and electronic games. He also regulary draws storyboards for films.

Juan Gimenez currently lives in Spain, on the Costa Dorada.

MŒBIUS

He is born under the real name of Jean Giraud in France, 1938.

Beginning in 1955, he illustrates several issues of a fiction magazine. His first comic strips appear in numerous French magazines. Later, he illustrates FORT NAVAJO, scripted by Charlier. This Western comic, better known afterwards under the name of its hero, BLUEBERRY, quickly becomes extremely successful in France. It becomes the signature series of Jean Giraud, who continues drawing it to this day.

In 1975, under the pseudonym of Mœbius, he collaborates in the founding of the magazine METAL HURLANT ("Screaming Metal"), to which he entrusts his first episodes of ARZACH and later AIRTIGHT GARAGE, two titles which take the comic world by storm. That same year, Mœbius meets Alexandro Jodorowsky, and they begin a long collaboration which will give rise most notably to the famous series, THE INCAL.

At the same time, Mœbius designs the sets for RIDLEY SCOTT'S ALIEN, and draws the storyboards for RENÉ LALOUX'S TIME MASTERS and WALT DISNEY'S TRON.

In 1984, Mœbius settles in the United States. There he pursues various interests, including drawing an episode of SILVER SURFER; he also continues to collaborate with several renowned filmmakers, among them James Cameron, to whom he lends his expertise for THE ABYSS, and Ron Howard, for whom he conceptualizes some of the characters in WILLOW.

He returns to Europe in 1989, where he continues his Blueberry series, works on his multimedia projects, and creates THE MAN FROM THE CIGURI, the sequel to AIRTIGHT GARAGE. He collaborates once again with Alexandro Jodorowsky on a new three-part series, MADWOMAN OF THE SACRED HEART, and on a book of erotic illustrations, ANGEL CLAW.

With more than sixty works of illustration and comics in his working repertory, Jean Giraud-Mœbius figures among the greatest comic book authors worldwide.

Alexanro Jodorowsky

Juan Gimenez

Jean Giraud - Mœbius

Photographed by Christophe Beauregard for Les Humanoïdes Associés S.A